ENVIRONMENTAL HEALTH - PHYSICAL, CHEMICAL AND BIOLOGICAL FACTORS

ADAPTIVE MANAGEMENT OF NATURAL RESOURCES

CONCEPTS AND APPLICATIONS

ENVIRONMENTAL HEALTH - PHYSICAL, CHEMICAL AND BIOLOGICAL FACTORS

Additional books in this series can be found on Nova's website under the Series tab.

Additional e-books in this series can be found on Nova's website under the e-book tab.

ENVIRONMENTAL HEALTH - PHYSICAL, CHEMICAL AND BIOLOGICAL FACTORS

ADAPTIVE MANAGEMENT OF NATURAL RESOURCES

CONCEPTS AND APPLICATIONS

DAMIAN LOWELL
EDITOR

New York

For permission to use material from this book please contact us:
Telephone 631-231-7269; Fax 631-231-8175
Web Site: http://www.novapublishers.com

Library of Congress Cataloging-in-Publication Data

ISBN: 978-1-63321-357-9

Published by Nova Science Publishers, Inc. † New York

CONTENTS

PREFACE

Our country's natural resource challenges today are more complex and more difficult to resolve than ever before. The loss of biodiversity, changing climatic patterns, spread of invasive species, alteration of landscapes, and many other problems pose serious threats to the long-term sustainability of America's natural resources. We urgently need to find new ways to address these problems. In particular, we need new methods and technologies to deal with the scale of the human footprint on the landscape, and new approaches to address the impacts of that footprint. A major challenge is to account for, and ultimately improve, our understanding of the long-term consequences of our actions. In this book, the authors use case studies to show how adaptive management can be used for both management and learning. The book focusese on practical applications in the areas of importance to Department of Interior managers – climate change, water, energy, and human impacts on the landscape. Adaptive management is presented as a form of structured decision making, with an emphasis on the value of reducing uncertainty over time in order to improve management. The first half of the book covers the foundations and challenges of adaptive management, and the second half documents examples that illustrate the components of adaptive management.

Chapter 1 – This report reviews the extensive and growing literature on the concept and application of adaptive management. Adaptive management is a central element of the Northwest Forest Plan and there is a need for an informed understanding of the key theories, concepts, and frameworks upon which it is founded. Literature from a diverse range of fields including social learning, risk and uncertainty, and institutional analysis was reviewed, particularly as it related to application in an adaptive management context. The review identifies opportunities as well as barriers that adaptive management faces. It concludes by describing steps that must be taken to implement adaptive management.

Chapter 2 – Our country's natural resource challenges today are more complex and more difficult to resolve than ever before. The loss of biodiversity, changing climatic patterns, spread of invasive species, alteration of landscapes, and many other problems pose serious threats to the long-term sustainability of America's natural resources. We urgently need to find new ways to address these problems. In particular, we need new methods and technologies to deal with the scale of the human footprint on the landscape, and new approaches to address the impacts of that footprint. A major challenge is to account for, and ultimately improve, our understanding of the long-term consequences of our actions.

For many important problems now facing resource managers and conservationists, adaptive management is a promising means of facilitating decision making and helping to resolve the uncertainties that hinder effective management. In this guide, the authors use case studies to show how adaptive management can be used for both management and learning. The authors focus on practical applications in the areas of importance to Department of Interior managers – climate change, water, energy, and human impacts on the landscape. Adaptive management is presented as a form of structured decision making, with an emphasis on the value of reducing uncertainty over time in order to improve management. The first half of the guide covers the foundations and challenges of adaptive management, and the second half documents examples that illustrate the components of adaptive management.

In: Adaptive Management of Natural Resources
Editor: Damian Lowell
ISBN: 978-1-63321-357-9

Chapter 1

Adaptive Management of Natural Resources: Theory, Concepts, and Management Institutions*

George H. Stankey, Roger N. Clark and Bernard T. Bormann

Introduction

A common feature of contemporary natural resource management issues is the underlying uncertainty regarding both cause (What causal factors account for the problem?) and effect (What will happen if a particular management strategy is employed?). These uncertainties are, in part, a product of the growing emphasis on long-term, multiscale, and integrative aspects of resource management. These involve multiple disciplinary perspectives, multiple jurisdictions and associated management objectives, and a growing concern with cause and effect over large spatial scales and long timeframes.

In the face of such issues, traditional approaches to scientific inquiry increasingly have been found inadequate, particularly with regard to the ability to predict consequences and effects. As many have argued (e.g., Herrick and Sarewitz 2000, Kuhn 1970), the central strategy of mainstream science has been to break phenomena into distinct components (disciplines), remove those components from their larger context, and identify mechanisms or processes to frame specific research questions. Although this paradigm has served science and society well (and will continue to do so), its capacity to contribute effectively to addressing many contemporary environmental problems is problematic.

These limits generally are acknowledged. Calls for ecosystem-based, integrative resource management explicitly or implicitly are grounded in the need for innovative institutional structures and processes (Cortner et al. 1996). Such approaches acknowledge the critical role of ongoing monitoring and evaluation as the basis from which learning would inform subsequent action. The iterative relation between learning and action is a hallmark of social learning planning models (Friedmann 1987).

---

* This is an edited, reformatted and augmented version of General Techincal Report, PNW-GTR-654, issued by the U.S. Department of Agriculture, Forest Service, Pacific Northwest Research Station, August 2005.

The concept of adaptive management has gained attention as a means of linking learning with policy and implementation. Although the idea of learning from experience and modifying subsequent behavior in light of that experience has long been reported in the literature, the specific idea of adaptive management as a strategy for natural resource management can be traced to the seminal work of Holling (1978), Walters (1986), and Lee (1993). These scholars have framed and articulated the idea of an approach that treats on-the-ground actions and policies as hypotheses from which learning derives, which, in turn, provides the basis for changes in subsequent actions and policies.

This contemporary concept of adaptive management has been applied across a range of resource sectors (agriculture, water resource management, fisheries, etc.) as well as a variety of sociopolitical contexts (Australia, Canada, Europe, Southeast Asia, South Africa, United States). The potential of adaptive management makes it an attractive strategy in situations where high levels of uncertainty prevail. It was this quality that led to adaptive management becoming a central component of the Forest Ecosystem Management Assessment Team (FEMAT) report (1993) and the subsequent Northwest Forest Plan (hereafter, the Plan) (USDA USDI 1994).

Implementation of the Plan began in 1994. The Plan's goal was to initiate an ecosystem-based management approach across 24 million acres (9.7 million hectares) of federal land in a three-state region in which sharp conflicts over objectives and values existed. These conflicts were exacerbated by high levels of uncertainty. Most existing science had been undertaken at the site or stand level, and its applicability at the watershed and regional level was not well understood. Moreover, the precarious status of endangered species and the diminishing extent of old-growth forests in the region combined to create a situation in which there was great concern—among citizens, managers, policymakers, and scientists—that it was important to be cautious in not aggravating the problem (figure 1). As a consequence, the Plan placed a heavy emphasis on reserves; about 80 percent of the planning region is in an administrative or statutory reserve. The reserve allocations were augmented by a set of restrictive standards and guidelines (S&Gs) that set performance standards for on-the-ground activities.

The Plan also acknowledged that improving understanding within and among the complex biophysical, social-economic-political systems in the region would require an increased emphasis on new knowledge. As a result, it called for adoption of an adaptive management strategy to gain new understanding. It proposed a four-phase adaptive management cycle (figure 2). In the first phase, plans are framed, based on existing knowledge, organizational goals, current technology, and existing inventories. In phase two, on-the-ground actions are initiated. Phase three involves monitoring results of those actions and, in phase four, results are evaluated. The cycle could then reinitiate, driven by emerging knowledge and experience. Results could validate existing practices and policies or reveal the need for alterations in the allocations, S&Gs, or both.

To facilitate the adaptive strategy, about 6 percent of the area was allocated to 10 adaptive management areas (AMAs) distributed across the three-state region to represent the diversity of biophysical and socioeconomic conditions (figure 3). The AMAs provided areas where there would be latitude to experiment with management practices, where the S&Gs could be tested and validated, and where innovative relations between land managers and citizens would be encouraged.

The Plan has been in place for more than a decade. A key question regarding implementation concerns the extent to which adaptive management has achieved its intended objectives; has it provided a framework within which key uncertainties contained in the Plan have been critically examined, tested, and, as appropriate, modified? A companion report[1] of this literature review describes this evaluation.

National Park Service.

Figure 1. In the Northwest Forest Plan, the diminishing extent of old-growth forests in the region has raised concerns whether these forests can be sustained and restored.

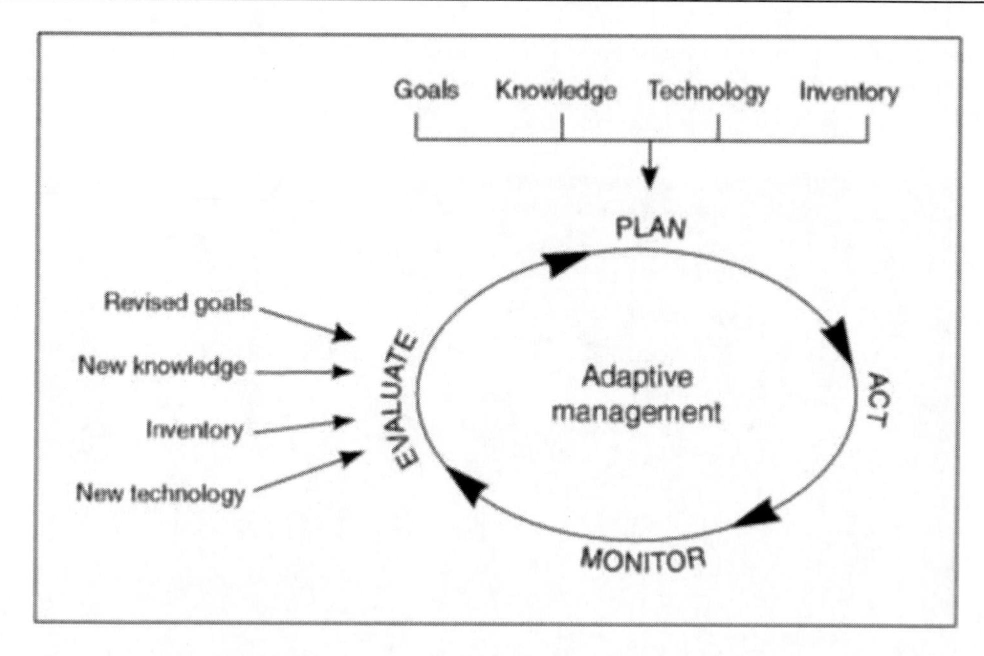

Figure 2. The adaptive management cycle (USDA USDI 1994: E–14).

The use of an adaptive management strategy for forest management has been given additional importance by the revised planning rule that guides implementation of the National Forest Management Act (NFMA). The new rule replaces the former chapter dealing with "regional planning," replacing it with "The Adaptive Planning Process" (see Forest Service Handbook 1909_12 chapter 20) and outlining the procedures responsible planning officials are to follow in implementing the new approach.

As suggested above, the adaptive management concept has been pursued in diverse fields, from agriculture, fisheries, and forestry in the natural resource arena to business and education. It incorporates diverse academic perspectives including learning theory, public policy, and experimental science. In some cases, relevant concepts and experiences derive from literature or policy experiments where the explicit notion of adaptive management is either absent or only of tangential interest. In this review, we have attempted to blend the results of substantive and technical analyses and discussions of the key conceptual components of an adaptive approach, with results from various implementation efforts.

The Concept of Adaptive Management

Haber (1964) traced the origins of adaptive management to the ideas of scientific management that took root in the early 1900s. The idea is linked to disciplines outside natural resource management; for example, adaptive management, or closely-related notions, are found in business (total quality management, continuous improvement, and learning organizations [Senge 1990]), experimental science (hypothesis testing [Kuhn 1970]), systems theory (feedback control [Ashworth 1982]), industrial ecology (Allenby and Richards 1994), and social learning (Korten and Klauss 1984).

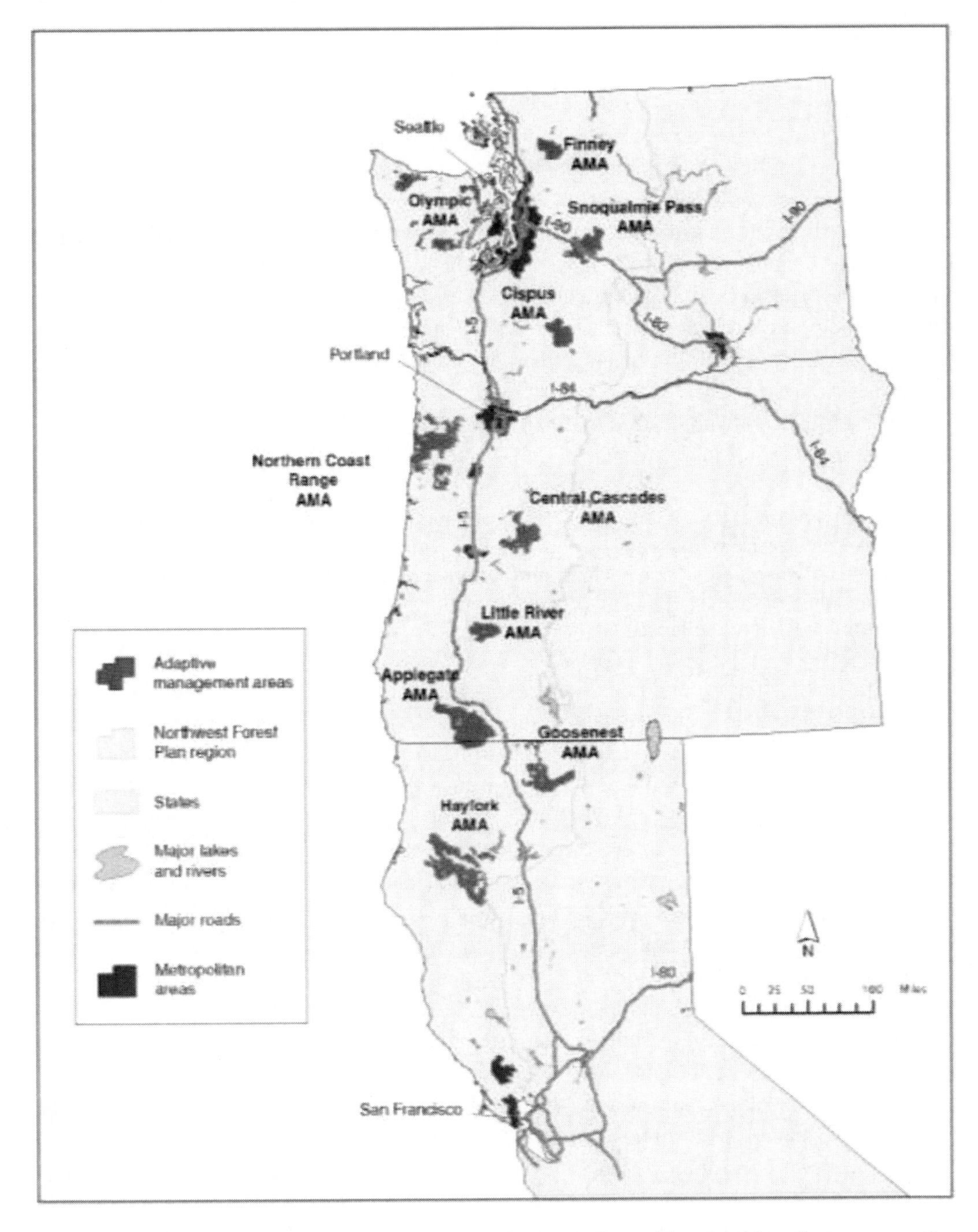

Figure 3. The 10 adaptive management areas in the Northwest Forest Plan provide a diverse range of biophysical, political, and socioeconomic conditions.

The concept has drawn particular attention in natural resource management (Bormann et al. 1999). In 1978, with publication of Holling's *Adaptive Environmental Assessment and Management*, its potential as a framework for dealing with complex environmental management problems began to be recognized. The subsequent publication of *Adaptive Management of Renewable Resources* (Walters 1986), *Compass and Gyroscope: Integrating*

Science and Politics for the Environment (Lee 1993), and *Barriers and Bridges to the Renewal of Ecosystems and Institutions* (Gunderson et al. 1995a) added increasing sophistication and elaboration to the concept and its potential. Key elements of adaptive management were explored in these texts; the importance of design and experimentation, the crucial role of learning from policy experiments, the iterative link between knowledge and action, the integration and legitimacy of knowledge from various sources, and the need for responsive institutions. A growing professional literature, reflecting a diverse body of interest and experience in application of adaptive management, has now developed. For example, in a literature search of the Cambridge Scientific Abstracts and SciSearch for 1997–98, Johnson (1999) found 65 papers that used adaptive management in their title, abstract, or keywords, covering issues from wildlife management, wetland and coastal restoration, and public involvement.

Holling (1995: 8) hypothesized that expanding interest in adaptive management has been driven by three interlocking elements:

> The very success in managing a target variable for sustained production of food or fiber apparently leads inevitably to an ultimate pathology of **less resilient and more vulnerable ecosystems, more rigid and unresponsive management agencies, and more dependent societies.** This seems to define the conditions for gridlock and irretrievable resource collapse [emphasis added].

In confronting these conditions, societies have sought strategies to forestall collapse. McLain and Lee (1996) reported that ethnographic evidence indicates humans long have relied on ad hoc hypothesis testing as a means of learning from surprise and increasing the stock of knowledge on which future decisions to use environmental resources are made. For example, Falanruw (1984) described how the Yap of Micronesia for generations sustained a high population despite resource scarcity by practicing adaptive techniques. Such techniques resulted in the production of termite-resistant wood and the creation and maintenance of coastal man-grove depressions and seagrass meadows to support fishing. The Yap altered their environment by using adaptive management processes; they undertook actions, observed and recorded results through story and songs, and codified practices through rituals and taboos. In short, at one level, the Yap experience embraces the modern concept of adaptive management: “policies are experiments: learn from them” (Lee 1993: 9).

Despite examples of the potential of an adaptive approach, contemporary examples of successful implementation are meager. In many ways, this seems paradoxical. On the one hand, adaptive management offers a compelling framework; i.e., learn from what you do and change practices accordingly. Yet, the literature and experience reveal a consistent conclusion; while adaptive management might be full of promise, generally it has fallen short on delivery. This dilemma is widely recognized (Halbert 1993, McLain and Lee 1996, Roe 1996, Stankey and Shindler 1997, Walters 1997), leading Lee (1999: 1) to conclude “adaptive management has been more influential, so far, as an idea than as a practical means of gaining insight into the behavior of ecosystems utilized and inhabited by humans.”

In part, the root of the difficulties might lie in the general level of familiarity with the notion of adaptation. As the Yap experience demonstrates, humans have long demonstrated the capacity to adapt to new information and contexts. Environmental stimuli provide feedback that inform us and modify subsequent behavior. Over time, individuals, groups, societies, and cultures learn to respond to changes; i.e, they adapt (or conversely, they don't and eventually inherit the consequences). There are a host of adaptive mechanisms, some more conscious and explicit than others. In sum, however, most people have personal experiences with "learning by doing" and as a behavior, it therefore seems obvious, even unexceptional.

Adaptive management, as discussed in the contemporary literature, stands in contrast to these conventional conceptions. Although it shares the general premise of learning by doing, it adds an explicit, deliberate, and formal dimension to framing questions and problems, undertaking experimentation and testing, critically processing the results, and reassessing the policy context that originally triggered investigation in light of the newly acquired knowledge. Thus, adaptive management in this context involves more than traditional incrementalism; learning derives from purposeful experimentation that, in turn, derives from deliberate, formal processes of inquiry, not unlike scientific study. In this sense, assertions that resource agencies have long been adaptive are less than persuasive.

Carl Walters, a contemporary proponent of experimental adaptive management, offered a pessimistic appraisal of recent progress. He noted "I have participated in 25 planning exercises for adaptive management of riparian and coastal ecosystems over the past 20 years; only seven...have resulted in relatively large-scale management experiments and only two of these experiments would be considered well planned in terms of statistical design" (Walters 1997: 2–3). His critique is grounded, in part, on the question of what constitutes an experiment. As used here, we see it "...loosely as an action whose outcome we cannot predict completely in advance or specific beforehand" (Bernstein and Zalinski 1986: 1024). To Lee (1999), experimentation has three components: (1) a clear hypothesis, (2) a way of controlling factors extraneous to the hypothesis, and (3) an opportunity to replicate the experiment to test reliability. However, the general disappointment about the effectiveness of implementing adaptive management derives from more than a definitional conundrum. There is a growing appreciation of the various cultural, institutional, social-psychological, and political-legal challenges confronting adaptive management (Miller 1999). But despite these challenges, there is a growing body of experience and scholarly commentary reporting alternatives for addressing them.

Key Premises of Adaptive Management

A foundational premise of adaptive management is that knowledge of ecological systems is not only incomplete but elusive (Walters and Holling 1990). Moreover, there is a growing conviction that expanding knowledge through traditional scientific inquiry will always be limited by resources and time. When these limiting factors are linked to the contextual conditions of resource scarcity, potential irreversibility, and growing demands, the need for new ways in which understanding and learning not only occur but directly inform decision making and policy processes becomes apparent (Bormann et al. 1994b). Adaptive management offers both a scientifically sound course that does not make action dependent on extensive studies and a strategy of implementation designed to enhance systematic evaluation of actions (Lee and Lawrence 1986).

As noted earlier, adaptive management has attracted attention for its emphasis on management experiences as a source of learning. This has produced a variety of phrases that emphasize the idea that adaptive management is learning to manage by managing to learn (Bormann et al. 1994a). This idea is not new; in a variation of the phrase, Michael (1973) entitled his book *On Learning to Plan—and Planning to Learn.* Whatever the particular phrase, the central idea is the presence of an iterative process that links knowledge to action (Friedmann 1987) and, conversely, action to knowledge (Lee 1993).

A critic of adaptive management might contend it is little more than a variant of Lindblom's (1959) "disjointed incrementalism" or, as commonly described, "muddling through" model. Natural resource management long has demonstrated an ability to build on previous actions and outcomes; policies are always subject to revision in the light of past performance (Kusel et al. 1996). Some learning occurs irrespective of the particular management approach taken; Gunderson (1999c: 35) commented, "trial-and-error is a default model for learning…people are going to learn and adapt by the simple process of experience." However, what distinguishes adaptive management from Lindblom's incrementalism is its **purposefulness** (Dovers 2003); agreed-upon goals and objectives serve as a basis against which progress can be measured and lessons gained. Adaptive management mimics the scientific method by highlighting uncertainties, specifying and evaluating hypotheses, and structuring actions to test those hypotheses through field application (Gunderson 1999c). In Walters' (1997) terms, adaptive management replaces management learning by ad hoc, trial and error (an incremental, evolutionary process) with learning by careful tests (a process of directed selection).

Use of the scientific method to improve understanding of the effects of natural resource management actions is not without limits and liabilities. Although adaptive management "rests on a judgment that a scientific way of asking questions produces reliable answers at lowest cost and most rapidly, this may not be the case very often" (Lee 1999: 4) and might even be the opposite; i.e., slow and costly. Although Walters (1997: 10) agreed that environmental management changes needed to resolve key uncertainties might prove unacceptably costly, he argued "most debates about cost and risk have not been…well founded, and appear instead to be mainly excuses for delay in decision making." It must also be recognized that the capacity of adaptive management to resolve value-based conflicts (e.g., forest management to meet economic as opposed to environmental objectives) might prove no more effective than traditional planning approaches.

There are many definitions of adaptive management (Bormann et al. 1999, Halbert 1993). As Failing et al. (2004) have observed, this widespread use of the term has propagated various interpretations of its meaning and, as a result, there are only vague notions about what it is, what is required for it to be successful, or how it might be applied. Not surprisingly, given recent attention by the scientific community, many definitions frame the discussion around a structured process that facilitates learning by doing; i.e., "adaptive management does not postpone action until 'enough' is known, but acknowledges that time and resources are too short to defer *some* action" (Lee 1999: 5). Holling (1978) and Walters (1986) specified two major components to the adaptive management process:

1. An effort to integrate existing interdisciplinary experience and scientific information into dynamic models to frame predictions about the impacts of alternative policies; this step performs three key functions:

- Problem clarification and enhanced communication among scientists, managers, and other stakeholders.
- Policy screening to eliminate options unlikely of doing much good because of inadequate scale or type of impacts.
- Identification of key knowledge gaps that make predictions suspect.

2. Design of a specific management experiment.

A third component to be added to this list links the results of a management experiment with the policymaking process; i.e., in light of the actions taken in an experimental setting, how do those results translate into changes in ongoing land management practices. In many ways, this third component is where the idea of "adaptive" comes into play, based on feedback from the results of experimentation.

These components contain important implications. Step 1 emphasizes the importance of problem framing, i.e., getting the question(s) right (Bardwell 1991, Miller 1999). This is a crucial phase; as Walters (1986: 9) noted, in system analysis terms, "bounding the problem" is where "most resource policy analyses go astray." For example, Smith et al. (1998) described how conflicts over appropriate management strategies for salmon in the Pacific Northwest are confounded by differing assessments regarding the underlying causes of the salmon's decline. Managers emphasize habitat loss, commercial fishers point to predators, and others identify water pollution. Failure to focus on problem definition can lead to inappropriate attention to symptoms and solutions (Van Cleve et al. 2003). Framing effective strategies in the face of such differences is also challenging because it is ultimately a social undertaking, involving a variety of perspectives and experiences; it must transcend its limitations as a technical-scientific endeavor. For example, Butler et al. (2001) argued that it is important that resource users (e.g., fishers) understand the benefits and costs associated with an adaptive approach. Without such information, adaptive adjustments can become nothing more than "tinkering in pursuit of fruitless equilibrium" (p. 797). Finally, the problem-framing phase needs to encourage a deliberate and informed "working through" process (Yankelovich 1991) in which options and their costs and efficacy are identified, debated, and evaluated. It can best achieve this through a process of informing all concerned of the inevitable risks and uncertainties involved. This helps focus future inquiry on the most important questions (or to gaps in knowledge that carry the greatest liability for the resource and stakeholders).

Two further comments on this process can be made. First, although step 1 refers to model development, it is the modeling **process** that is particularly important as it is the means through which the three principal functions of step 1 are achieved. Whether a specific model emerges from this or not is not necessary; the modeling process helps facilitate learning, which in turn, informs future decisions. McLain and Lee (1996) noted that evidence from case studies in British Columbia and the Columbia River basin supports the idea that models can be useful for enhancing information flow by stimulating discussion among stakeholders about values, goals, objectives, and management options.

Second, this learning process is information-intensive and requires active, ongoing participation from "those most likely to be affected by the policies being implemented" (Lee 1999: 7). This emphasizes the social and political aspect of adaptive management. Lee (1993: 161) noted "Managing large ecosystems should rely not merely on science, but on *civic* science; it should be irreducibly public in the way responsibilities are exercised, intrinsically technical, and open to learning from errors and profiting from successes." Civic science, he argues, is a political activity; "Ecosystem-scale science requires political support to be done…Learning in such a setting cannot take place without active political support; there are too many ways for things to go wrong without it" (Lee 1993: 165). This view was reiterated in FEMAT: "People will not support what they do not understand and cannot understand that in which they are not involved" (FEMAT 1993: VII–113). It is this political element of adaptive management that provides Lee's "gyroscope" (i.e., "the pragmatic application of politics") to the companion notion of the "compass" of science (i.e., "the idealistic application of science to policy") (Lee 1993: 10–11).

ALTERNATIVE MODELS OF ADAPTIVE MANAGEMENT

Walters and Holling (1990) suggested three ways in which adaptive processes could be structured. First, there is an evolutionary or trial-and-error model[2] (Holling 1978; Kusel et al. [1996] used the term **incremental adaptive management** and Hilborn [1992] referred to it as a **reactive** approach). Under such approaches, the results of external decisions and choices are used to frame subsequent decisions that, we hope, lead to improved results. In many ways, this form of adaptive management is reminiscent of muddling through, in which some learning inevitably results from whatever management experience is undertaken. There is no purposeful direction to it and one simply reaps whatever benefits derive from earlier experiences.

Second, there is the concept of passive adaptive management; Bormann et al. (1999) used the term **sequential learning**. In it, historical data are used to frame a single best approach along a linear path assumed to be correct (i.e., there is a belief that the underlying assumptions and antecedent conditions that were applicable earlier still prevail). This model applies a formal, rigorous, albeit post facto analysis to secondary data and experiences as a means of framing new choices, understanding, or decisions.

Passive adaptive management can be informative. Walters and Holling (1990) reported on work in the Florida Everglades focused on the effects of various interventions in the region's water regime. The work was driven by the single hypothesis that wildlife in the area require a natural pattern of water availability. This led to changes in both the timing and distribution of waterflows, with the intention that the plan would be the first step in a longer, iterative testing process that could lead to shifts in hydrological regimes (figure 4). This could produce, over time, important benefits for the ecosystem. Nonetheless, Walters and Holling (1990) argued that alternative hypotheses should have been framed; e.g., what were the effects of natural changes in nesting habitat outside the area? Such alternatives could have led to different analyses and, potentially, to new management strategies.

Two fundamental problems limit passive adaptive approaches. First, such approaches can confound management and environmental effects because it is often unclear whether observed changes are due to the way the land was treated or to changes in environmental factors (e.g., global warming). Second, such analyses can fail to detect opportunities for improving system performance when the "right" model and the "wrong" model predict the same results and the system is managed as though the wrong model were correct.

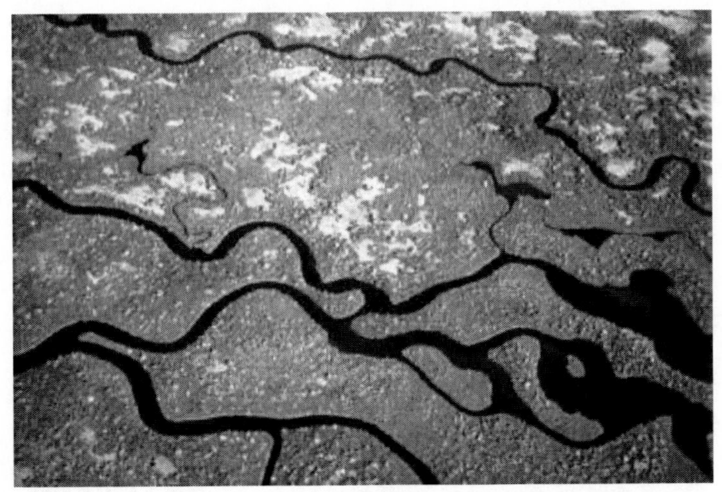

National Park Service.

Figure 4. The timing and distribution of waterflows in Florida's Everglades is the focus of an adaptive management study designed to protect the region's ecosystem.

Active adaptive management is a third model. It differs from other versions in its purposeful integration of experimentation into policy and management design and implementation (Kusel et al. 1996). In other words, policies and management activities are treated as experiments and opportunities for learning (Lee 1993). Active adaptive management is *designed* to provide data and feedback on the relative efficacy of alternative models and policies, rather than focusing on the search for the single best predictor. Bormann et al. (1999) referred to active approaches as examples of **parallel learning** because they involve the design of suites of policies that can be directly and simultaneously compared and evaluated.

Adaptive management is inevitably a sociopolitical action as well as a technical-scientific undertaking. Kusel et al. (1996) addressed the social dimension in terms of the relationships among scientists, resource managers, and the public. They argued that adaptive processes, as opposed to traditional resource management approaches, are "fundamentally about changing the relationships between these three groups" (Kusel et al. 1996: 612–613). **Participation-limited adaptive management** focuses on the interface of scientists and managers. Here, citizens stand apart from the dialogue and interaction between scientists and managers and are connected only via traditional public information venues, such as public meetings. This model is consistent with the historical reliance on the expert-driven, command/control approach that characterized social reform planning during much of this century. In contrast, **integrated adaptive management** can dramatically change the relationships among participants, with the public engaging as peers and partners with their manager and scientist colleagues to build active working relationships among themselves (Buck et al. 2001). Such relationships are central to the ideas of social learning.

In summary, the literature reports a variety of ways to undertake adaptive management, although there are no standard templates to guide decisions about what is best. The focus on formal learning, however, coupled with creation of forums that facilitate improved problem identification and framing; mutual, ongoing learning; and informed debate about alternatives, options, and consequences are central elements that an adaptive approach seeks to foster.

But the question of how to structure and design an adaptive management process is only one challenge confronting resource managers. Next, we turn to a variety of issues, challenges, and problems identified in the literature; each of these must also be addressed effectively if adaptive approaches are to be effective.

LEARNING: A DRIVER AND PRODUCT OF ADAPTIVE MANAGEMENT

The concept of learning is central to adaptive management and is grounded in recognition that learning derives from action and, in turn, informs subsequent action. Lee (1999) argued that the goal of implementing management experiments in an adaptive context is to learn **something**; he also argued that surprise is an inevitable consequence of experimentation and that it is often a source of insight and learning. Yet, such observations beg the question as to what learning is. What is implied when we say we have learned? Does any change in the phenomena being studied represent learning or only certain changes? Is learning measured at the individual level, at some small collective (e.g., a planning team), or at a larger, organizational level? A related question concerns the idea of organizational learning. Is it simply the sum of individual learning within the organization, or does collective learning take on an emergent quality (i.e., properties that can be attributed to a system as a whole, but not to any individual components [Clayton and Radcliffe 1996]) that exceeds the sum of that held by individuals within the organization? What distinguishes change based on learning from other change (Parson and Clark 1995)? Further, how do we best organize to learn? Michael (1995: 484) contended "there are two kinds of learning: one for a stable world and one for a world of uncertainty and change." In a world of rapid change and high uncertainty, acquiring more facts—data—might not be as important as improving the capacity to learn how to learn, or what Ackoff (1996) has described as deutero-learning. In other words, what might have once facilitated learning might no longer do so.

Four commonalities emerge from the learning literature. First, learning is initiated when some dilemma or tension appears regarding a problem. For example, previously held assumptions might prove unfounded or dysfunctional and there is a need to learn how to proceed (Mezirow 1995). Or, new problems emerge for which little is known. In either case, the discrepancy between what is known and what is needed creates tensions that can only be resolved through learning. Of course, learning itself can be anxiety-producing (Michael 1995), so the need for and benefits of learning must outweigh the anxiety produced during the learning process.

Second, much learning derives from experience and, in particular, from experiences in which mistakes were made. Mistakes or what operations research would call "negative feedback" have the potential to be powerful sources of insight. Dryzek (1987: 47) described it as a "highly desirable quality." Such feedback and the learning it can produce, is a central premise of adaptive management (Lee 1993). However, as we shall discuss in more detail later, risk-aversion at both the individual and institutional levels can combine to hamper such learning. A management culture that ignores or even punishes failures and mistakes can seriously retard the learning process.

Third, learning almost always involves change. This begins by acknowledging a dilemma, discussed above, that initiates learning behavior. The subsequent learning must then be transferred into the organizational system in such a way that future behavior (policies, programs) reflects the new information. Also, because an organization is imbedded in a wider biophysical and socioeconomic environment, where change is ongoing, it must also be open to continuous learning that permits it to operate effectively as that wider environment changes. Again, this is the fundamental premise of the adaptive management process. However, individual and institutional behavior is often biased toward maintenance of the status quo, and such continuous change can be difficult and anxiety-producing (Parson and Clark 1995). As Dovers and Mobbs (1997) concluded, adaptive, learning institutions do not always survive.

Fourth, learning involves what is referred to as reframing. Reframing is the process of reinterpreting the world in light of alternative perspectives and values. In simple terms, it involves seeing problems in a different way. Because reframing can lead to critiques of current policies, processes, or structures, it can be psychologically uncomfortable and resisted by others. Nonetheless, the reframing process is an essential component of a learning organization and can be facilitated by purposefully incorporating diverse perspectives on planning teams (Yorks and Marsick 2000).

Learning manifests itself in distinctive forms, including data, information, knowledge, understanding, and wisdom (Ackoff 1996). **Data** are simply "1s and 0s" stored in a spread sheet. They reflect and describe actual observations. **Information** includes data, but provides details regarding who, what, when, and where. **Knowledge** concerns questions relative to "how to" and offers insight as to how a system might be managed. **Understanding** clarifies questions related to cause and effect; here, we begin to understand why systems act and respond as they do. Finally, **wisdom,** as Ackoff (1996: 16) suggested "is the ability to perceive and evaluate the long-run consequences of behavior." Adaptive management, in a contemporary sense, is particularly concerned with advancing learning at the knowledge, understanding, and wisdom levels.

What Is Learning?

Opinion is divided on the question of what it means to learn. The debate turns on whether the appropriate indicators of learning involve a change in cognition (a change in knowledge), a change in behavior (observable changes in organizational practices and policies), or both (Tsang 1997). Given an emphasis in the adaptive management literature on the role of action informed by knowledge, it seems that appropriate indicators of learning necessarily involve both cognition and behavior. Knowledge that lacks a link to action would seem to constitute little more than facts on the shelf; conversely, action that lacks a base in improved knowledge is little more than hopeful activity. Thus, learning would seem to require both a cognitive dimension as well as an observable behavioral manifestation grounded in improved knowledge. It is also clear that significant barriers grounded in organizational processes, belief systems, or other factors act to stymie the acquisition of improved knowledge or its implementation into action. Inkpen and Crossan (1995) drew attention to how organizational norms and sanctions can operate to stymie learning or thwart behavioral change, effectively maintaining the status quo.

Learning encompasses knowledge acquisition; to say we have learned implies that we know more than previously (which might include that we now know how little we knew). Michael (1995) argued that learning implies more than increasing the stock of facts: it suggests we know what needs to be done, how to do it, whether it worked, and how to apply learning to emerging consequences. In other words, learning is not an end in itself, but a means to informing subsequent action. He also argued that learning involves what "must be unlearned" (p. 461). We all have certain trained incapacities, and learning must acknowledge and accommodate these. However, to do so can evoke feelings of psychological discomfort, denial, anger, and fear (Miller 1999). Michael (1995: 468) added "…most people under most circumstances are not all that eager to learn…most…are content with believing and doing things as they have always been done" and individuals (including scientists) are rewarded for maintaining and sustaining certain beliefs and behaviors because these are "the way things are and should be."

The literature identifies a number of factors that facilitate or constrain the learning process. Various categories can be defined: structural/organizational (e.g., laws, policies, organizational structure), sociocultural (e.g., values and beliefs), emotional (e.g., concerns with risk and failure), and cognitive (e.g., whether additional information leads to learning or simply overload).

The literature also discusses the concept of learning styles. People learn in different ways. For example, learning differs in terms of **perception** (the way in which information is taken in) as well as in the way we **order** that information (the way we use the information we perceive). There are differential capacities in dealing with information in a concrete versus abstract or conceptual manner. And, there are a variety of ways in which people best organize the information around them: as facts, as principles, in terms of relevance, or in terms of underlying reasons.

Learning occurs through various means. A classroom teacher, for example, facilitates the learning process for his or her students. In terms of new knowledge (i.e., learning) about the world, Lee (1999) and Marcot (1998) suggested that experimentation is not the only way to learn, or even the most obvious way. Table 1 depicts different learning modes.

The processes through which learning occurs change as people age. This has led to a significant literature of adult learning theories. As with many of the literatures we examine in this review, this is a large, diverse area. However, for our purposes, this literature suggests that a key feature of the learning process for adults is that learning occurs not so much through incremental accumulation of understanding (e.g., more facts), but via "leaps" of understanding when existing information is examined in a new light. In particular, this process is triggered by a critical reexamination or reframing of an individual's past experiences and underlying beliefs and assumptions about the world. This critical assessment, in turn, leads to a reassessment of previous understanding and, more importantly, to a realization that new options and alternatives exist and that previous presumed constraints and bounds on one's thinking no longer prevail. Reflection is a key element of this process because it offers people an opportunity to determine whether previous assumptions still are relevant and applicable to the decisions that face them (Mezirow 1995). These views of learning are especially important in an adaptive context, given that one's assumptions are open to critical review by other parties in the problem-framing stage and previous experiences, subject to new perspectives and insight, can provide opportunities for identifying plausible hypotheses (policies) for critical examination in the field.

Table 1. Modes of learning

Each mode of learning	makes observations...	and combines them...	to inform activities...	that accumulate into usable knowledge.	Example
Laboratory experimentation	Controlled observation to infer cause	Replicated to assure reliable knowledge	Enabling prediction, design, control	**Theory** (it works, but range of applicability may be narrow)	Molecular biology and biotechnology
Adaptive management (quasi- experiments in the field	Systematic monitoring to detect surprise	Integrated assessment to build system knowledge	Informing model-building to structure debate	**Strong inference** (but learning may not produce timely prediction or control)	Green Revolution agriculture
Trial and error	Problem-oriented observation	Extended to analogous instances	To solve or mitigate particular problems	**Empirical knowledge** (it works but may be inconsistent and surprising)	Learning by doing in mass production
Unmonitored experience	Casual observation	Applied anecdotally	To identify plausible solutions to intractable problems	**Models of reality** (test is political, not practical, feasibility)	Most statutory policies

Source: Lee 1999: 3.

Perhaps the most controversial issue with regard to the notion of learning and the processes and structures that facilitate it links to two related questions: is learning a technical or social process (or both) and, as noted earlier, is organizational learning simply the sum of individual learning within that structure or is it an emergent product that is more than the sum of the learning of individuals within the organization?

Is Learning the Result of Technical Processes, Social Processes, or Both?

Advocates of learning as a technical process argue that it primarily involves processing information. For example, Argyris and Schön (1978: 2) took the position that learning "involves the detection and correction of error." In this view, management organizations, such as the Bureau of Land Management, constitute social technologies designed to perform a specific set of tasks; i.e., they represent a working model of a theory for solving a particular and specific set of problems. To the extent that this system works well, it reflects the notion of **single-loop learning** (Argyris and Schön 1978). Single-loop learning occurs when individuals perceive a mismatch between their intentions (i.e., what they wanted to have happen) and actual events (i.e., what actually takes place) and then take steps to correct that action. Such a process is driven by existing assumptions about how a system works and that the organization has the capacity to detect error or problems and solve them.

However, new problems often emerge or are reconfigured in ways that are neither recognized nor soluble by the theory embodied in the current organizational structure. For example, the FEMAT (1993) social assessment chapter addressed the changing nature of the demands, uses, and values associated with forests in the Pacific Northwest and the increasing inability of current organizations and policies to deal with those changes. To overcome these types of problems requires rethinking the fundamental purposes, rules of operation, and assumptions on which an organization is founded so that it has the capacity to more accurately diagnose the problems of theory driving the search for answers to practical problems. This involves a capacity for critical self-examination; it requires what Argyris and Schön defined as **double-loop learning**. Such learning addresses basic questions of why problems occurred in the first place, whether the management solution is correct, and if not, how to make corrections (British Columbia Ministry of Forests 2000). Through hypothesis testing and theories about how the world works, and the comparison of the results of these tests against experience, the potential for informed, grounded revision is enhanced. But, as Argyris and Schön (1978) warned, organizations often inhibit this type of learning because it requires critical assessment of current organizational assumptions, beliefs, and norms.

The concept of double-loop learning has important implications for adaptive management. First, it reemphasizes the importance of sound problem-framing processes (Bardwell 1991). The way in which questions and problems are framed directly affects the way in which solutions are defined and pursued. Second, as noted above, redefining the questions and problems confronting an organization can be a painful process; it often reveals liabilities and shortcomings in organizational culture and structure that, if left untended, leave that organization at risk. For example, in the case of the conflicts between environmentalists and timber interests in the Pacific Northwest during the 1990s, reliance on technical assessments and studies—key elements of contemporary resource management culture—has done little to resolve the crippling debate; "the failure of technical studies to assist in the resolution of environmental controversies is part of a larger pattern of failures of discourse in problems that put major societal values at stake. Discussions of goals, of visions of the future, are enormously inhibited" (Socolow 1976: 2). Under these conditions, any management approach, including adaptive management, that fails to embrace the social and value-based dimensions of a problem as well as technical dimensions, will be limited in its ability to foster resolution.

An alternative conception of learning focuses on learning as the product of social processes. Here, learning results from participation and interactions with others in social life (Easterby-Smith and Araujo 1999). The distinguishing feature of this conception is that learning is a process of social construction; i.e., people "construct" reality in ways meaningful to them. From this perspective, scientific data do not hold objective, unequivocal meaning, but are given meaning and interpretation by people. Thus, in natural resource management, problems characterized by complexity and uncertainty also will be characterized by varying interpretations and, by inference, different solutions.

Within natural resource organizations, knowledge is continually constructed and reconstructed as different people interact with one another and as new information becomes available. Thus, a social constructivist perspective also focuses attention on the ways in which institutional structures and processes can facilitate, enhance, or constrain the construction and dissemination of learning. Thus, the notion of "learning to learn," an idea promoted by Ackoff (1996) in the theoretical literature, as well as in the Northwest Forest Plan, becomes an important feature.

Clearly, the emphasis in adaptive management on learning, although important, also introduces an extraordinarily complex arena. At the core of this is the reality that learning needs to derive from **both** technical and social processes. For instance, we might hypothesize that the lack of learning is attributable to the lack of data and the associated knowledge. In other cases, the lack of learning derives not from the lack of information, but the manner in which it is presented (abstract vs. concrete), the social processes and structures (or lack thereof) to facilitate communication and discussion among organizational members, or because of its presentation as a set of principles as opposed to its potential relevance to a particular problem. In any case, the information is effectively inaccessible and learning fails to occur.

Organizational Learning or Learning Organizations?

A second, correlate question regarding learning concerns the relationship between individual learning and a more collective form of learning that ascribes to the organization.

Two predominant arguments are found in the literature: (1) organizations do not learn; what is called "organizational learning" is simply the sum of individual learning, and (2) organizations as a system can learn, with that learning reflecting an emergent quality that exceeds the sum of individual learning.

Proponents of the first argument argue that "organizational learning" only occurs when individual learning becomes institutionalized into organizational norms and memory (Watkins 1996). Organizational learning, in this schema, becomes successful when structures exist to encourage individual learning and there are processes for transferring and codifying that learning into the organization.

The alternative view contends that organizational learning surpasses the sum of individual members. For example, Yorks and Marsick (2000: 253) argued that "groups can learn as discrete entities in a way that transcends individual learning within the group." This perspective views organizations as systems that have the capacity to produce learning characterized by an emergent quality; i.e., the collective learning is more than the sum of individual learning. As suggested earlier, the notion of emergent properties derives from systems thinking; from this perspective, individual learning becomes a necessary, but not sufficient, condition for organizational learning. It further contends that "new" learning emerges through the interaction of organizational members who collectively create new knowledge not attributable to any one individual. It thus also becomes closely linked to the idea of learning as the product of social processes.

Although knowledge is clearly linked to the learning process, it is also an issue in and of itself and there is a significant literature surrounding it. Knowledge is defined in a variety of ways; e.g., Webster's dictionary defines it as "the sum of what is known…the body of facts accumulated…in the course of time." But a common view of the concept of knowledge is that it reveals the way in which we know the world.

The concept of adaptive management implies the **production** of knowledge (through policy and management actions); it also implies that such knowledge is **transmitted or distributed** among various interests (scientists, managers, and citizens) and that it is **used**. In our assessment of adaptive management, the issue of knowledge is critical. In terms of knowledge production, questions arise as to where knowledge is created and by whom. In the positivist model that underlies modern scientific inquiry, research scientists are seen as the principal knowledge producers. The formal knowledge that emerges from scientific inquiry is a powerful form of knowing; done properly, it is characterized by being replicable and reliable. Scientific inquiry attempts to analyze the world through formal concepts and theories, involving the systematic dissection of problems into smaller components (reductionism) and isolating and controlling external factors (Holzner and Marx 1979, Kloppenburg 1991). There is also a presumption that scientific inquiry is independent of social context; i.e., it is value-free and not subject to social influence (Gurvitch 1971). The value of such inquiry and knowledge is deeply imbedded in modern resource management philosophy and institutions; it is a fundamental element of the social-reform movement in planning (Friedmann 1987) and the foundation of modern forest management.

There is growing recognition of the importance of alternative forms of knowledge or knowing. Known variously as "personal," "local," "experiential," or "indigenous" knowledge, this form of knowing emerges from experience gained through living, working, and playing in the world. Buttolph and Doak (2000) argued that such knowledge, rather than being less valid or legitimate, highlights other ways of seeing and knowing (fig. 5). Yet, such knowledge often is trivialized, marginalized, or rejected in modern planning processes. Kloppenburg (1991: 529) suggested that scientific knowledge has come to hold "undisputed intellectual hegemony" with local knowledge relegated to the "epistemic peripheries." Thus, the core precept of social reform planning—that science serves society—is predicated on the caveats that (1) only a certain form of knowledge (formal science), controlled by a certain group of people (scientists), is admitted to the decision making arena and (2) science possesses accurate insight as to society's needs.

Gary Wilson, USDA Natural Resources Conservation Service.

Figure 5. **There are many ways of "knowing" the world around us.** Knowledge grounded in technical understanding and the personal or experiential knowledge gained from living and working in a place are both needed.

Yet, there is also growing recognition of the limits of formal, scientific knowledge in resolving the complex issues confronting society. Often, such knowledge is inadequate for the kinds of analyses required and for the development of functional predictions and useful management strategies (Friedmann 1987). Herrick and Sarewitz (2000) argued further that high levels of scientific complexity mean that predictive scientific assessments inherently are limited in their ability to guide policy development. They contend that a more appropriate and useful role for such assessments would be in conducting **ex post** evaluations, a role consistent with adaptive approaches that seek insight through critical analyses of policy implementation results.

Recognizing the limits of formal knowledge is critical to fashioning programs of knowledge creation, distribution, and utilization in an adaptive management model. In this model, citizens and managers are seen not only as the source of values and objectives or as reviewers and reactors to proposals, but also the source of improved understanding and knowledge about the complex systems with which we are concerned. If barriers to the recognition, acceptance, and legitimization of alternative forms of knowledge exist—cognitive, structural, or procedural—the adaptive process will be adversely affected.

Finally, the literature highlights the importance of two forms of knowledge; **explicit** knowledge (so-called articulated or substantive knowledge, composed of facts, data, etc. and recorded in books, reports, etc.) and **tacit** knowledge (the intuition, perspectives, beliefs, and values created as a result of experience). As Saint-Onge (1996) noted, tacit knowledge forms a "mental grid" within which explicit knowledge is filtered and interpreted. "[T]acit knowledge is made up of the collective mindsets of everyone in the organization. Out of its experience, the organization assumes a unique set of beliefs and assumptions through which it collectively filters and interprets how it sees the world and reacts to it" (Saint-Onge 1996: 10). Thus, tacit knowledge becomes a critical factor in shaping the paradigm underlying how some group (e.g., resource managers) establishes professional standards, behavioral norms, and conceptual approaches to problem-solving (Kuhn 1970, Wondolleck 1988). In short, it can be a powerful, formative, and enduring type of knowledge.

Assessing knowledge, from whatever source, and using it to build understanding, framing such understanding into questions and hypotheses, formulating options and alternatives, and testing, monitoring, and validating the outcomes of these alternatives requires explicit design (Haney and Power 1996). The issue of adequate design permeates the adaptive management literature; in essence, it addresses a straightforward question: How and when do we know we have learned something? Does the action taken lead to the results observed, or were results due to other, perhaps unknown, factors or chance (Bednar and Shainsky 1996)? Real learning is dependent on a capacity to discern the answer to such questions. This challenge explains why the protocols, methods, and philosophy of science have attracted attention in the adaptive management literature, for it represents a method of inquiry grounded on establishing cause-and-effect relationships. As Lee (1999: 4) noted, "in principle, the scientific approach leads to reliable determination of causes; in practice, that means being able to learn over time how management does and does not affect outcomes…an experimental approach may be costly and onerous in the near term, but it is probably the only way to root out *superstitious* learning—erroneous connections between cause and effect."

Adequate research design to facilitate sound learning in adaptive management experiments often is lacking (Walters 1997). In part, this derives from a persistent lack of formal and systematic documentation. Lee (1993) pointed to the critical need for an intellectual paper trail that provides an explicit record of the chain of reasoning underlying any action. Lacking such documentation, it is difficult if not impossible to later review assumptions, data, methods, analytical treatments and so on to help understand why differences between outcomes and predictions occurred.

In northeast Victoria, Australia, Allan and Curtis (2003) reported on a project designed to use an adaptive approach to developing alternative options for the management of salinity. The implementation of on-the-ground works, such as tree planting, became the highest priority, but program administrators failed to recognize that such plantings could be viewed as experimental treatments. Coupled with a lack of formal monitoring, the sum effect has been that it has proven difficult to assess the efficacy of different salinity management options and an opportunity to learn more systematically from implementation has been lost.

Walters (1997) identified design of management experiments as the second key step in the adaptive management process. He concluded, with some notable exceptions, that literature reporting well-designed field applications of adaptive management is sparse. In particular, few efforts included either adequate controls or designs for replication. He also was critical of efforts that have not progressed beyond continued investments in baseline information gathering and in complex simulation modeling. He concluded "what probably drives these investments is the presumption that sound predictions (and, hence, good baseline policies) can somehow be found by looking more precisely, in more mechanistic detail, at more variables and factors" (Walters 1997: 3).

Walters' comments suggest limits to the benefits derived from more data or better models. In discussing adaptive management planning models for riparian and coastal ecosystem situations, he described some of the complex technical issues that need to be accommodated in experimental design. One example involves problems that derive from cross-scale linkages between physical/chemical and ecological processes. Hydrodynamic and chemical processes that operate on short time scales and fine spatial scales must interact with ecological processes in the marine and estuarine setting that operate over long periods and broad spatial scales. To resolve the burdensome computational process, the various subcomponent models are sometimes decoupled, but the process of disconnecting inextricably connected systems leads to problematic outcomes. He concluded "we must rely on empirical experience, not modeling or physical principles, to tell us how much averaging and selecting we can safely do" (Walters 1997: 5).

Lee (1993) identified three circumstances that reinforce the need to consider large-scale experimentation. First, large-scale ecosystems manifest emergent properties that do not occur or cannot be detected at smaller scales; salmon abundance in the Columbia River system is different from that in any stream within the larger system. Second, some effects are too small to observe at the laboratory scale; e.g., the introduction of a new chemical as a constituent of an agricultural fertilizer might not result in the immediate death of fish when lab tested, but when released in a larger, more complex system, could lead to adverse effects. In the absence of explicitly designed controls, these effects might go undetected until it is too late. Third, ecosystem-level interventions might already be underway in the form of existing policy decisions, or decisionmakers might be unwilling (or unable) to postpone action until more is known. Such events provide opportunities for large-scale experimentation, as long as it is recognized that the outcomes of the experiments are poorly understood and the potential for significant adverse impacts (e.g., extirpation) exists.

Lee (1999) argued that explicit, well-designed experimentation also helps address what he describes as two social misdirections of learning. First, the concept of the "regression to the mean" needs to be kept in mind. Many environmental issues with which we struggle today initially attracted attention because of their extreme condition (e.g., declining fisheries), but in a dynamic world, extreme events often are followed by less-extreme ones; "there is a regression to the mean, not because something has been remedied but simply because the mix of fluctuating causal factors has changed…[producing]…fertile ground for erroneous conclusions" (e.g., because we presume some intervention either caused or resolved the problem, when in fact, it was driven by external conditions or cycles) (Lee 1999: 4).

Second, he elaborated on the idea of superstitious learning, the illusion that something has been learned when "evaluations of success are insensitive to the actions taken" (Levitt and March 1988: 326). Explanations for why something worked or failed often are incorrect; we simply might not understand why things worked as they did, and the relation to any particular intervention or event is only coincidental. Lee concluded that when "resource managers are held to standards that have no grounding in ecological science, the more likely it is that accountability itself will induce superstitious learning" (1999: 5).

Lee (1993: 74) concluded "for some policy questions, statistical concepts promote understanding of the nature of the policy judgments required." His argument derives from the idea that although technical and statistical analyses are necessary, their presence is not sufficient to fully inform policymakers of the effects of their actions. He elaborated on this in a discussion of the distinction between the statistical concepts of type I and type II errors. A type I error occurs when what one believes to be true actually is false. This is a fundamental precept on which Western law is founded. As a society, we accept that it is better to occasionally let a guilty party go free than it is to punish an innocent person. Science is also a field in which avoidance of type I errors is part of the culture; we tend to be conservative in accepting something as true. In the case of environmental management, we impose high standards of proof because we are reluctant to accept something as true (e.g., the minimum acceptable level of water quality for salmon survival), because if we later find this to be false, we might have already imposed irreversible impacts on the species.

Type II errors occur when something is rejected that later turns out to be true. For example, a scientific panel convened in New Brunswick, Canada, sought to determine whether the use of pesticides to control a spruce budworm epidemic was implicated in the deaths of children from a disease called Reye's syndrome. Central to their deliberations was the question of what constituted scientific proof of harm. The provincial government took the view that only **incontrovertible** scientific proof of harm would lead them to change their spraying policy (Miller 1993). A survey in the province identified over 3,000 cases of illness with symptoms similar to Reye's syndrome (at the time, Reye's syndrome was not a reportable illness in the province and most physicians were unfamiliar with it). A subsequent screening, focused on identifying the specific disease, reduced this to about a dozen, excluding from consideration the possibility that pesticides might have been a factor in the etiology of some, or all, of the excluded cases. A scientific panel reviewing the data concluded no incontrovertible scientific proof existed to establish a causal link between spraying and the disease. Their conclusion reveals the difficulty in determining the etiology of a rare disease; it provided little in terms of understanding the effects of spraying on more common viral diseases plaguing the community. By focusing on a narrow hypothesis (Reye's syndrome), the "panel appears to have a committed a type 2 error by accepting false negative findings…"; the analytical methods chosen to conduct the study provided an "opportunity to look for clearly defined needles in a poorly documented haystack" (Miller 1993: 567). Reliance on a narrow, analytically confined problem definition served to obscure the real problem, providing instead a dubious scientific basis for sustaining the status quo policy position.

What are the implications for adaptive management? It reveals the kind of tension that exists in many natural resource management debates today, including those between forest management and endangered species management. On the one hand, the role of regulatory agencies, such as the Fish and Wildlife Service, is to avoid type I error; i.e., they want to avoid approving an action, taken to be sound (true) based on the best science, that later proves to be unsound (false). For example, a proposal to test an alternative silvicultural technique in riparian zones might be supported by considerable evidence and theory showing it would have beneficial effects on stream conditions. However, a strong predisposition to avoid type I errors would deny such a proposal on the grounds that implementation of the experimental treatment might endanger salmon. On the other hand, denying the experiment might engender a type II error, given that the experiment might prove more beneficial to salmon than the current prescription. Moreover, denial limits opportunities for learning in the face of uncertainty (Wildavsky 1988). Nonetheless, there remain concerns about the social and environmental costs of allowing type II errors to occur, and the argument is made that a shifting burden of proof calls for an unequivocal demonstration that no adverse consequences will eventuate from some policy (M'Gonigle et al. 1994). The resulting tension between these perspectives creates a "Catch-22" dilemma: permission to experiment is denied until such time as clear, rigorous, and unequivocal scientific evidence is available, but permission to undertake the work that might produce such evidence also is denied. This dilemma leads to a discussion of risk and uncertainty.

RISK AND UNCERTAINTY

The concepts of risk and uncertainty are inextricably linked to adaptive management. In the most basic terms, if there were no risk or uncertainty, there would be no need for adaptive management. It is only when we are faced with uncertainty as to what is the most appropriate course of action that the concept of adaptive management becomes a strategy that offers a means of acting. Although the terms of risk and uncertainty often are used interchangeably, they are not synonyms. Risk is typically defined as the possibility that an undesirable state of reality might occur as a result of natural events or human activities (Renn 1992). Risk definitions typically involve a known probability distribution; e.g., we know there are only 5 chances out of 100 that a particular catastrophic event will occur in the next 100 years.

Risk is increasingly recognized as a social construct, holding different meanings for different people. Risk analysis and assessment involve efforts to estimate both the probabilities of occurrence and the severity or seriousness of such occurrences, along with the distribution of those effects. Risk assessment, then, becomes more than a technical endeavor, involving social judgments of importance of varying events along with equity issues related to the distribution of costs and benefits (Mazaika et al. 1995). The challenge is all the more formidable because many of the consequences with which we are concerned are not only unanticipated, they cannot be anticipated (Schwarz and Thompson 1990).

Uncertainty is a more complex issue. Typically, uncertainty involves situations in which the probability distribution is not known. One major concern is when risk and uncertainty are treated as synonyms; e.g., treating a situation as one involving risk when, in reality, it is a situation of uncertainty. Walters (1986) suggested three types of uncertainty: (1) that which arises from exogenous (i.e., external) disturbances; (2) uncertainty about the values of various functional responses (e.g., how production rates of a species vary according to size of the stock); and (3) uncertainty about system structure, or more basically, what are the variables one should consider.

In some situations, uncertainty is assumed away; e.g., former Secretary of the Interior Bruce Babbit's promise of "no surprises" in the implementation of new policies for management of endangered species (Reichhardt 1997). Another response is to replace the uncertainty of the resource issue (e.g., Is the species threatened?) with the certainty of a process, be it a new policy or new institution. Gunderson (1999b) described the 9-year adaptive management experiment in the Florida Everglades where the uncertainty of chronic resource issues (e.g., water levels and distribution) has been replaced by the certainty of a planning process and formalization of interactions between management agencies and stakeholders. These processes are not without benefit—they have helped spawn ideas for future action—but whether they also produce learning or reduce risk remains unknown. To protect certain species in the Pacific Northwest, guidelines were instituted calling for surveys before ground-disturbing effects take place, extensive regional surveys within specified timeframes, and the development of management plans for these species (Nelson 1999). However, the survey and manage requirement also has stifled experimental management and research policies that could provide under-standing needed to ensure species survival.

Bioregional assessments, such as FEMAT, have been driven by growing unease regarding the risks and uncertainties (regarding both biophysical and socioeconomic systems) facing society. FEMAT (1993) concluded that the levels of risk and uncertainty facing policymakers are greater than acknowledged (they are also why an adaptive approach was seen as essential). Accounting for risk is an essential part of such assessments because of the stochastic nature of processes that characterize ecological and socioeconomic systems. The risks associated with predicting outcomes can be offset to some degree by explicit portrayal and discussion of the underlying cause-and-effect relationships and working assumptions about those relationships (Thomas 1999: 19).

Uncertainties are inevitable, which is why surprise (Gunderson 1999c, Lee 1993) must be formally incorporated into the adaptive management process. Lee (1995) identified two critical elements confronting society's efforts to achieve sustainability: biological uncertainty and institutional complexity (which we turn to shortly). He argues that in moving the "unsustainable vitality of industrialism to a sustainable order, learning from experience is the only practical approach" (p. 228). He noted the difficulties facing those who seek guidance for what to do; namely, data are sparse, theory is limited, and surprise is unexceptional. Wilson (2002) argued that removing uncertainty from public discussion can retard learning by engendering the belief that adequate knowledge exists (e.g., Gunderson's [1999b] "spurious certitude"). If the pretense of surety dominates policy discussions (Dovers and Mobbs 1997), science can be discredited when events lead to contrary outcomes, thus diminishing the ability to manage sustainably. Uncertainties play a key role in the adaptive management process; highlighting them helps frame hypotheses and initiate actions to test them (Gunderson 1999c). If results confirm the hypotheses, then actions and policies can be adjusted accordingly. If we fail to confirm the hypotheses, nonetheless we have acquired useful information that can inform revised hypotheses, which can be subsequently tested.

However, this process, however logical and straightforward, depends on two key conditions; there must be both permission **and** a willingness to experiment. This means explicitly confronting uncertainty and risk. Unfortunately, uncertainty is not always acknowledged. "Judged from a traditional point of view, uncertainty and the lack of predictive capabilities equal ignorance" (Pahl-Wostl 1995, cited in Wilson 2002: 332). If acknowledging and operating under uncertainty are deemed unacceptable—within the organizational culture, through external sanctions such as statutes, or because of public scrutiny and intervention—then adaptive management is not possible. In other words, if action in the face of uncertainty must be accompanied by an assurance that nothing will go wrong, then we have a recipe for inaction. As Wildavsky (1988) argued, requiring that no action be undertaken without a prior guarantee of no risk is a restrictive decision criterion. Volkman and McConnaha (1993) contended that invocation of the Endangered Species Act in the Columbia River basin effectively has halted any attempt at active adaptive management experimentation, in large part because of the uncertainties of experiments on fish. A consequence of such a stance is "no new trials, no new errors—but also no new experience and hence no new learning" (Wildavsky 1988: 31). Unfortunately, as Huber (1983) has remarked "Statutes almost never explicitly address the lost opportunity costs of screening out a product" (cited in Wildavsky 1988: 35). In other words, the costs of lost learning are seldom accounted for when experimentation is restricted or prohibited.

Resistance to experimentation can also derive from those who perceive adverse impacts on their interests. For example, Johnson and Williams (1999) described how the short-term risks to harvest levels (fish, wildlife) associated with experimentation can mobilize opposition to adaptive approaches. Implementation of a regulatory experiment can mean that traditional harvest objectives are replaced with learning objectives, with a result that hunters or fishers bear the costs of the experimentation in the form of reduced take levels.

Lang (1990) offered an alternative typology of uncertainty:

1. Uncertainty concerning the specific problem and its context. This leads to conflicts over what data are needed, what new research should be undertaken, how forecasts might be improved, and how strategies such as risk assessment might better inform discussions.
2. Uncertainty about how to address the problem, with respect to both ends and means. This means that clear policy guidance is required, but it also implies a thorough assessment about what the problem is before the search for solutions begins (Bardwell 1991, FEMAT 1993).
3. Uncertainty concerning what others might do about the problem. This means that dealing with uncertainty must also embrace processes of collaboration and coordination.

These different forms of uncertainty are interrelated. For example, to act without clearly understanding what the problem is likely will result in a failure to reduce uncertainty. To act in an absence of understanding what others are doing risks inefficiency, duplication, and the possibility of working at cross purposes. Such concerns underlie the social, political, and collaborative nature of the challenges facing adaptive management (Buck et al. 2001, Lee 1993).

Dealing with risk and uncertainty are major challenges to adaptive management. Despite the difficulty of operating under such conditions, principles to guide organizational behavior do exist. Ludwig et al. (1993: 36) suggested such principles are "common sense"; e.g., consider a variety of hypotheses and strategies; favor actions that are robust to uncertainty, informative, and reversible; monitor; etc. However, effective and informed operation in the face of uncertainty is confounded when institutions responsible for adaptive management implementation are, at their core, risk averse; the term is not used in a pejorative sense, but simply means that organizational behavior emphasizes the prevention of harm (Wildavsky 1988).

Estill (1999: 20) (emphasis added) argued that "one of the **primary** roles of Forest Service managers in American society is to guard against risk…protecting against risk is one of the few principles managers can use to identify appropriate points of balance and compromise in gut-wrenching situations." Her comments are not without merit, but they imply an organizational capacity for control that is neither possible nor realistic. "The primary expectation of adaptive management is the unexpected…systems are unpredictable" (Gunderson et al. 1995b: 490). It hints at the kind of spurious certitude to which Gunderson (1999b) referred and ignores how embracing risk (and uncertainty) is requisite to learning and discovery (Michael 1995).

INSTITUTIONAL STRUCTURES AND PROCESSES FOR ADAPTIVE MANAGEMENT

Holling hypothesized that success in managing a target variable for some commodity output leads inevitably to "an ultimate pathology of less resilient and more vulnerable ecosystems, more rigid and unresponsive management agencies, and more dependent societies" (1995: 8). Our attention now turns to the issue of institutions—including those "rigid and unresponsive management agencies"—but also the array of laws, policies, and other rules by which we live. Why have institutions, designed to better serve our needs and wants, become barriers to the very goals to which we aspire?

Institutions generally are taken to include the array of mechanisms society employs to achieve desired ends (Cortner et al. 1996). Scholars (e.g., Ostrom 1986) have described institutions as sets of rules, as standards of behavior, or as political structure, yet there is little agreement of what the term means or how to undertake studies of them. Some argue that institutions also include norms and values and their interaction with the rules and behaviors (McCay 2002). Institutions are both formal and informal and profoundly affect how society defines problems of significance and organizes itself to formulate responses to those problems.

Wilson (2002) offered insight into this question and although his focus was on marine management, his conclusions seem applicable in other resource contexts. He contended that the scientific uncertainty associated with managing complex systems has created a more difficult conservation problem than necessary because current governing institutions assume more control over natural processes than in fact is possible. He concluded that managing complex, uncertain systems that manifest highly adaptive qualities requires that the governing institutions also be adaptive and learning-driven.

In a critique of efforts to implement adaptive management policies in riparian and coastal ecosystems, Walters (1997: 3) identified four reasons for the low success rates observed. "All," he noted, "in some sense, are **institutional** reasons" (emphasis added): (1) modeling for adaptive management planning has been supplanted by ongoing modeling exercises, (2) effective adaptive management experiments are seen as excessively expensive or ecologically risky, (3) there is often strong opposition to experimental policies by people protecting self-interests in the bureaucracies, and (4) there are value conflicts within the community of ecological and environmental interests.

Gunderson concurred, noting how a "rigidity or lack of flexibility in management institutions and extant political power relationships has precluded adaptive experiments" (1999c: 35), even in situations, such as the Everglades, where the ecological system had sufficient resiliency to accommodate such experimentation. Lee (1993) devoted attention to the need for improved institutional structures and processes to facilitate the practice and exercise of civic science. In his assessment, the challenges of overcoming "inappropriate social organization" (p. 153) loom as a major barrier to the successful implementation of adaptive management. Organizations and policies often are entrenched (e.g., Western water law) in the pursuit of some particular goal, yet institutions find learning leads to a change in goals, which in turn trigger changes in order, structure, power, and other institutional currencies. Such changes produce ambiguity and stress, and a common response is to resist the changes that produce those effects. Lee (1999: 7) observed that "adaptive management is an unorthodox approach for people who think of management in terms of command."

In a review of six case studies from North America and Europe, Gunderson et al. (1995b: 495) reported that one of the major insights revealed during their analyses was the "extreme nature of the recalcitrance or inertia of institutions, and the almost pathological inability to renew or restructure." They concluded that the extent and depth of the resulting institutional rigidity has led to a failure to effectively engage and resolve underlying resource conflicts. Based on a study of adaptive management efforts in New Brunswick, British Columbia, and the Columbia River Basin, McLain and Lee (1996) concluded that efforts fell short of the promise of adaptive management because of an over-reliance on rational-comprehensive planning models, a tendency to discount nonscientific (i.e., personal or experiential) knowledge, and a failure to create processes and structures to facilitate shared understandings among stakeholders.

Scholars generally are in accord as to the central role of institutions in implementing adaptive approaches. Indeed, Gunderson (1999a: 54) argued that if there is any hope for the future of natural resource management, it must be founded on "developing and creating new ways to think about and manage issues of the environment…it is time to rethink the paradigms or foundations of resource management institutions." Yet, McLain and Lee (1996: 446) observed "the adaptive management literature pays little attention to the question of what types of institutional structures and processes are required for the approach to work on a large-scale basis." Lee (1995: 230) also acknowledged the institutional challenge; "…it is not clear how the adaptive approach can work in the presence of institutional complexity."

Yet the reality is that we do have institutions in place—management agencies, laws, policies, standards and guides, norms and belief systems—and we need to consider how the adaptive management concept, with all its compelling appeal and logic, can be made to work. In particular, we face the challenge of framing innovative and effective alternatives to structures and processes that have long been in place and that have a long history of successful implementation. This results in a "if it ain't broke, why fix it?" mentality. Wilson (2002: 332) described the dilemma facing management institutions in framing innovative models for the future:

> We can create institutions nicely tailored to a particular scientific theory and preconception of the nature of the uncertainty (we believe) we face, or we can design institutions on an alternative basis, one that assumes as little as possible about the nature of causal relationships and emphasizes the role of collective learning and institutional evolution. The appropriateness of one or the other approach would appear to depend on the state of our scientific knowledge or, alternatively, our ability to test and validate.

McLain and Lee (1996) argued that the rationale for adaptive learning in management systems rests on three key elements: (1) rapid knowledge acquisition; (2) effective information flow; and (3) processes for creating shared understandings. These constitute a useful framework within which to examine some of the literature relative to the institutional challenges of implementing adaptive management.

INCREASING KNOWLEDGE ACQUISITION

The concept of scientific adaptive management rests on the notion that the formal methods of scientific inquiry, based on hypothesis testing, represent the most effective and efficient means of acquiring new knowledge. However, evidence from case studies from across North America and around the world question this assumption. A variety of factors contribute to this problematic assessment. As noted earlier (e.g., Walters 1997), heavy reliance on models has contributed to a bias in knowledge acquisition of quantifiable data. This leads to distortion in the problem-framing stage, resulting in a tendency to frame problems as technical in nature when often they involve value-based issues (e.g., what goods and services are desired from the forests of the Pacific Northwest?). Despite the prevailing conception of objective science, many issues confronting resource managers and scientists today are **trans-science**: "Though they are, epistemologically speaking, questions of fact and can be stated in the language of science, they are unanswerable by science; they transcend science" (Weinberg 1962; cited in Lowe 1990: 138). Allen and Gould (1986) arrived at a similar conclusion, describing a set of problems they define as wicked that arise from disputes over questions of importance and preference, rather than technical merit. Genetic or bioengineering and large-scale environmental modifications are examples of such undertakings.

Thus, increasing the rate of knowledge acquisition is confounded by differences in problem perception and the corollary issue of the types of knowledge required in addressing such problems. Challenges also derive from deeply imbedded convictions that scientific knowledge is more valid than other forms of knowing (e.g., personal or experiential knowledge) and that decisions based on scientific knowledge will lead to better decisions (McLain and Lee 1996).

Finally, the literature points to the cost of data acquisition for adaptive management as a major hurdle; the necessary monitoring and evaluation efforts to support adaptive approaches are expensive in both money and time. The risks associated with adaptive experimentation are judged excessively costly. McLain and Lee (1996) noted that the costs of monitoring and evaluation were especially controversial in the New Brunswick spruce budworm experiments because only one stakeholder was responsible for both the action and its evaluation. In the Pacific Northwest, the North-west Power Planning Council attempted to avoid this by involving a wide range of stakeholders in the monitoring and evaluation process (McLain and Lee 1996). This proved costly, raising questions as to whether it would prove possible to continue to do this into the future. Although Walters (1997) acknowledged that the costs of adaptive experimentation can be great, he contended that costs in the form of risks to resources are even greater. He argued that the debate about costs and risks lacks adequate evaluation and scrutiny, suggesting that cost concerns tend to be used more as an excuse for avoiding contentious decisions.

There is a complex asymmetry in the distribution of the risks and costs of adaptive management. For instance, Walters (1997) noted that the costs of experiments that might benefit fish typically are borne largely by economic interests (agriculture, industry). It has been estimated that losses to commercial and recreational fisheries in British Columbia owing to experimental reduction of hatchery salmon releases could range from $10 to $100 million per year (Perry 1995). Although acknowledging that costs can be substantial for economic interests, Walters (1997) argued that these interests will inevitably face costs associated with change, given the nature of shifting public interests and concerns. He observed (Walters 1997: 11):

> If...there is even a 10% chance that legislative or legal decisions will result in massive and permanent policy change, the expected cost (0.1 x cost of massive change) of trying to maintain current policy would be radically higher than the cost of an experiment to demonstrate that radical change is unnecessary.

The tension between short-term costs and long-term benefits produces a complex situation. Any benefits of treatments undertaken today to manipulate biophysical systems likely will not appear until later; their costs, however, are borne by today's individuals, organizations, and society. There are both financial and risk costs involved. As Walters (1997: 11) noted, the "legacy of response information (i.e., learning) from these treatments will mainly be useful to the next generation of managers and users." The time differential between incursion of costs and receipt of benefits contributes to tensions between managers and scientists, on the one hand, and political and public officials on the other. For example, Lee (1993) described a goal of the Columbia River Basin Fish and Wildlife Program as doubling salmon populations over an unspecified time. This goal implies that salmon restoration must be seen as a long-term undertaking, measured in generations of salmon. These long-term undertakings are being dealt with in a political and budgeting world of 1- to 3-year cycles and the similarly short tenure of members of the Northwest Power Planning Council (McLain and Lee 1996).

The timeframes involved and the asymmetry between costs and benefits also have implications for how experimentation risks are perceived, particularly by resource managers. Volkman and McConnaha (1993: 6) argued that because the benefits of learning about flow-survival relationships on the Columbia River are less clear than the costs posed by dramatic flow manipulations, the concept of adaptive management faces an unusually difficult test in practice; i.e., "how (can) biological risks and political considerations be accommodated while taking an aggressive approach to learning?" Gray (2000), reviewing progress on the North Coast AMA, concluded that managers perceived the "inordinate amount of supporting data, energy, and political support" needed to modify any of the standards and guidelines "not worth their while" (p. 18). At one level of analysis, such unwillingness makes sense; the potential costs of an experiment can be substantial, immediate, and personal, whereas any benefits are long-term, uncertain, and diffuse. However, this complex issue warrants more attention and we shall return to it in discussing the attributes of an adaptive institution.

The issue of rapid knowledge acquisition also raises questions about who participates in the knowledge creation process and how. Wondolleck (1988) argued that resource management organizations must provide opportunities for joint fact-finding. "To facilitate both meaningful and satisfying participation by national forest users in agency decision making requires that each group and individual be operating with equal information" (p. 198). It is critical that people not only understand the implications of different outputs, but that they are "a part of the process that goes about obtaining and analyzing this information" (Wondolleck 1988: 198).

ENHANCING INFORMATION FLOW

Once information is acquired, it must be communicated to stakeholders—those charged with decision making and implementation responsibilities and those whose interests might be affected by an impending decision. In traditional agency planning processes, the information communication process is often restricted to the former group (i.e., decisionmakers and implementers). In democratic systems open to public scrutiny, a host of stakeholders influence the decision making process; in effect, they possess veto power. McLain and Lee (1996), for example, pointed to how adaptive management modelers in New Brunswick assumed that federal and provincial foresters and politicians were the key political actors in the debate over spruce budworm spraying, thereby marginalizing members of the environmental movement. Later, environmentalists moved to mobilize public opposition to the spraying program, effectively stymieing implementation.

The efficient flow of information to relevant parties, both internal and external, is impacted by information complexity. Environmental problems, and potential solutions to them, require qualified, technical expertise. This problem is confounded by the inability of many research scientists to communicate results and potential implications clearly. Resource managers, faced with heavy workloads, different priorities, and limited staff and time, often are not eager to wade through research papers and reports, particularly given that doing so might require them to change their behavior (Michael 1973).

Efforts to span boundaries and create more efficient and effective flows of information have attracted attention. Addressing the challenge of an organization striving to adapt to change, Michael (1973) noted two underlying aspects that require attention. First, organizations often work to eliminate the need for boundary spanning in the first place (and its turbulent consequences) by attempting to control their environment; e.g., a resource management agency tries to convince a skeptical public that its programs are appropriate and sound. Second, and somewhat contrary to the first, the "societal conditions that create the need for [boundary spanning] mean that the potential for controlling the environment will be low" (Michael 1973: 238).

The idea of boundary spanners (i.e., people to link across functions such as research and management) has attracted the attention of natural resource agencies. Ideally, these would be people with sound backgrounds in both management and science. Although there are arguments as to where these individuals might reside organizationally (i.e., within the research or management organization?), in general, the idea is that they would help communicate and interpret research results to managers, provide feedback to researchers on the results of the application of results, and play a coordinating role among the respective players.

The concept of spanning has drawn only limited attention in the adaptive management literature. One notable exception is reported from Australia, involving application of an adaptive management strategy for the water cycle in the urban fringe of three areas. In each experiment, the presence (or absence) of an **institutional champion** for the project was identified as a key factor. For example, in the Tuggerah Lakes project, north of Sydney, the presence of such a champion was deemed critical in obtaining acceptance of the adaptive management approach by both the local council and community participants (Gilmour et al. 1999). The authors noted that the absence of such a champion, or in one case, the loss of that person to another job, resulted in little enthusiasm and a reduced likelihood of successful implementation. They concluded there is a strong need for a person within the lead management agency to act as the change agent—the institutional champion. Such persons should be sufficiently influential in the decision making process to ensure a continued focus on the experiment-review-feedback cycle; they also need excellent communication skills to work at multiple levels within and outside the organization. The relative scarcity of such individuals makes efforts to implement adaptive management strategies vulnerable to organizational change.

An absence of champions also can detract from the ability to capitalize upon learning and knowledge from outside the immediate area of concern. Ewing et al. (2000: 455) argued that "ensuring the incorporation of, and access to, R & D [research and development] outcomes from nonlocal projects is...problematic since there is not necessarily a 'champion' who is aware of other research and ensures that it is incorporated." They cited the absence of a local champion in a rural planning exercise in southwest Western Australia as having an adverse impact on efforts to ensure effective, ongoing communication between, and within, various subgroups working on the project.

In reviewing efforts to implement adaptive management in the operation of the Glen Canyon dam and its effects on the Grand Canyon ecosystem, the National Research Council evaluation team observed "an advocate is needed for the adaptive management experiments themselves, particularly regarding their scientific coherence and the long-term integrity of the Grand Canyon ecosystem. There is currently no voice among the stakeholders that represents the interests of these scientific experiments" (National Research Council 1999: 61).

The critical role of key individuals in fostering and facilitating the flow of information, and serving as champions of adaptive management also was recognized by Gunderson et al. (1995b). They cited three roles for such individuals: visionary activist, respected integrator, or rebel bureaucrat. The latter two roles are especially critical, given their position within the bureaucracy. Such persons have a particular capacity to speak "truth to power" (Wildavsky 1979), an important role when the results of adaptive experiments run counter to prevailing policy and the status quo. In an early evaluation of adaptive management in Canada, the lack of a "wise person" to shepherd projects was identified as a major factor contributing to project failures (ESSA 1982). Duinker and Trevisan (2003) concluded these individuals were especially critical in gaining understanding and support among front-line staff that might otherwise have been reluctant to participate cooperatively in the project. These advocates served as teachers who helped create and sustain the organizational support necessary for effective implementation.

Feedback is a key process in enhancing information flow, particularly in an adaptive management context. The flow of information from an action back into the decision making process provides a basis for evaluating that action and for guiding future actions. In particular, negative feedback, reporting on the negative consequences of some action, is especially informative; i.e., "learn from your mistakes." Such feedback is critical in situations involving complexity and uncertainty. As Dryzek (1987: 47) noted,

> negative feedback is the presence of deviation-counteracting input within a system...In an environment of complexity and uncertainty, one cannot completely understand that environment...As a substitute for perfect understanding of the insides of

> the "box" (i.e., the environment), any intelligent choice mechanisms will be so structured as to respond to signals emanating from the "box."

As an ideal, feedback is the process through which decisionmakers acquire the information necessary to deal with uncertainty. Walters (1986: 233) observed that "it is a truism to state that the best management decision to make at any point in time is some function of all the information available at that time." He also argued that effective feedback policies are designed not only to report on the results of previous actions, but also provide some anticipation of future responses to those actions. In short, feedback informs decisionmakers not only about what has occurred, but what is likely to happen in the future.

When effective feedback processes are absent, adaptive management is handicapped. Yet, organizational receptiveness to feedback, particularly negative feedback, often is hampered by structural and cultural barriers that resist acknowledging information contrary to existing practices, policies, and beliefs (Miller 1999). In some cases, this stems from efforts to avoid overloading people with excessive amounts of information, especially given that the implications of that information might not be clear. Often, however, resistance stems from more deep-seated sources. Michael (1973: 271) argued "People have structured organizations (and organizations have structured people) to avoid unfamiliar feedback...Organizations arrange to receive a minimum of turbulence-generating feedback, and to use as little as possible of that to generate further turbulence." He added "Feedback which is disrupting because it is unfamiliar is also avoided by structuring the feedback retrieval process so that it selects from the environment only those signals that are compatible with the structure and norms of the organization." In sum, feedback is not assimilated, processed, and evaluated evenly; the process is highly selective, filtering out, discounting, or ignoring that which stands contrary to contemporary policies, beliefs, or dogma. As Schiff (1962) has recounted with regard to the role of fires in longleaf pine forests of the Southern United States, research inconsistent with prevailing policy was suppressed, and the published work only surfaced 6 years after completion. Feedback was interrupted because of its conflict with the dominant ideology.

With regard to the concept of feedback, there is a lack of clarity as to the effects of differing characteristics of that feedback. For example, in applications of continuous improvement models in a business context, often there is relative clarity and agreement as to what information is critical in a feedback loop and what implications it contains. Moreover, such feedback becomes apparent relatively quickly in the system; changes in demand for products, impacts of price changes or changes in product quality, etc. However, in ecological systems, feedback is often both delayed, perhaps substantially so (years or decades) and the meaning and implications of change are often neither clear nor agreed upon. Indeed, the very complexity of ecological systems that has made the concept of adaptive management appealing also contributes to the limits of the utility of feedback in assessing performance, causation, or management implications. Although it is correct that adaptive processes have been productively used in business contexts, fundamental structural differences in the underlying complexity of ecological systems mean that feedback processes must be understood to be inherently uncertain. As Roe (1998: 96) has remarked "The more you search complexity, the more perverse feedback cycles you will find."

Given the critical role of feedback in the adaptive management model, what can be done to overcome or mitigate these hampering effects? Michael (1973) suggested two important strategies, one internal and the other external. First, he called for creation of organizational structures and norms that sustain and reward learning. This means cultivating a capacity and acceptance of self-criticism that encourages critical thinking and openness to new information. It is also a critical step in restoring trust among competing interests (Michael 1995). Second, it is important in the external environment that there be a capacity to force openness and responsiveness to feedback. Here, the onus is on the ability of voluntary or other external organizations to both provide feedback and to insist upon organizational attention to it.

CREATING SHARED UNDERSTANDINGS

McLain and Lee (1996: 445) concluded "the scientific adaptive management approach has failed to provide adequate forums for the creation of shared understandings among stakeholders." The emphasis here is not on trying to create a single perspective, or even a consensus of values and meanings, but to create civic places where respect, legitimacy, and credibility of diverse interests and perspectives can be fostered (Shannon 1987). However, such forums are notably absent in the natural resource arena and across society in general.

Yankelovich (1991) called for creation of forums designed to facilitate the process of **working through**, a phrase drawn from psychology that describes the process of coming to grips with change. In part, this involves processing information, but even more so, it involves confronting the pressures and conflicts that engulf individuals and organizations and which they must, somehow, accommodate. He went on to point out "society is not well equipped with the institutions or knowledge it needs to expedite working through. Our culture does not understand it very well and by and large does not do a good job with it" (p. 65). The concept is especially germane here, for in the process of creating shared understandings and achieving the condition where individuals and organizations have a capacity to understand, respect, and legitimize diverse interests, values, and perspectives, new processes and institutions might be needed. The lack of such processes and institutions, however, can constrain the ability to implement adaptive management.

Walters (1997) contended that self-interest and unresolved value conflicts often combine to stymie adaptive management. For example, Allan and Curtis (2003) described efforts to use electromagnetic mapping as a means of assessing the extent to which salinity had affected agricultural lands in northeast Victoria, Australia. Although introduction of the technique raised community interest in the salinity issue, the lack of a framework describing what the mapping was intended to achieve, how the information could be used, and how it related to other information collected in the area contributed to confusion and a subsequent disillusionment with the program.

But this leaves the vexing question: If current institutional structures and processes lack capacity to behave adaptively, what type of organization would be capable of doing so? We examine this issue next.

INSTITUTIONAL ATTRIBUTES FACILITATING ADAPTIVE MANAGEMENT

Two central issues confront efforts to more effectively implement adaptive management. First, what would an adaptive management organization look like (and implicitly, how would it differ from existing structures)? Second, what transformation processes must be undertaken?

We can examine these questions from two perspectives. First, there is a body of empirical work examining the various factors associated with "successful" applications of adaptive management as well as those where adaptive management has fallen short of expectations. Second, there is a more theoretically-based literature that discusses the necessary attributes of adaptive organizations. Combined, the literature provides important insight about the steps needed to implement adaptive approaches in natural resource management.

Ladson and Argent (2002) conducted a comparative assessment of three projects in the United States in which adaptive approaches were used—the Columbia, Colorado, and Mississippi Rivers—and compared those results with efforts to implement adaptive approaches in Australia's Murray-Darling Basin. Their purpose was to gain a better sense of the conditions that affect efforts to implement adaptive management. They concluded there were different degrees of success in the three case studies, but that the Colorado River program—involving efforts to evaluate the impacts of alternative low-flow releases through Glen Canyon Dam on ecological conditions in Grand Canyon National Park—was the most successful (fig. 6). They identified seven variables that contributed to this success: (1) the relatively simple jurisdictional situation (the area involved only the state of Arizona and Grand Canyon National Park); (2) few points of possible legal or political intervention in the river's management; (3) credible science was present, with all reports subject to peer review and an independent scientific panel overseeing research efforts; (4) system modeling on the Colorado was "complex enough to obtain credibility but simple enough that it could be completed and used in a reasonable time frame" (p. 96); (5) managers could point to early achievements in experimental management, such as a 1996 beach-building flood that gained both scientific and political support; (6) a sense of community among the various stakeholders that enabled a consensus regarding goals and objectives of the project; and (7) the project was, in a sense, the "only game in town," requiring that all interested stakeholders participate in the process.

Mapstone (2003), describing experiences in implementing strategies for reef line fisheries on Australia's Great Barrier Reef, expanded on the desirable contextual situations for successful implementation of adaptive management. These included (1) the presence of options for alternative management strategies (an idea closely aligned to Bormann et al.'s [1999] concept of "multiple pathways"), (2) specific objectives for assessing performance, (3) effective monitoring and feedback systems, (4) cross-sectoral support from stakeholders, (5) clear and open mechanisms for information transfer, (6) assurance of continuity of organizational and governmental commitment, and (7) protection against political expedience. Meppem and Bellamy (2003), reviewing efforts to implement a 4-year research and development project on integrated resource use planning in the central highlands of

Queensland, Australia, added three additional "cornerstones of a healthy adaptive management system": (1) support for individuals and sectors to develop their own planning capacity, (2) facilitating understanding of both socioeconomic and biophysical processes within the systems, and (3) strong institutional arrangements that facilitate negotiations among interests.

Consistent with theories of adaptive management, negative feedback on the performance of alternative approaches can be important sources of insight. In Ladson and Argent's (2002) critique of adaptive management on the three American river systems, they were particularly critical of the situation on the Columbia River. Here, they found four contextual conditions that constrained efforts, including (1) "modeling wars" between specialists, with the result that excessive attention focused on details of modeling, rather than its use as a basis for problem framing; (2) institutional complexity involving both multistate and multinational jurisdictions; (3) the stultifying effects of the Endangered Species Act, which constrained experimentation; and (4) the complex web of values at stake, leading to a resistance to changes in the status quo. The vast scale of the Columbia River experiment also increased the likelihood that the institutional, socioeconomic, and biophysical complexity found across the region would lead to unintended consequences, exacerbating concerns among stakeholders about impacts on their interests and values (Butler et al. 2001).

Meppem and Bellamy (2003) also acknowledged problems from the central highlands project in Queensland, including (1) lots of plans but little on-the-ground evidence of implementation, (2) lack of understanding of relationships within and between systems, (3) an organizational inability to respond to change (i.e., an inability to move beyond the status quo), and (4) inadequate problem definition, driven in part because not all stakeholders were involved.

National Park Service.

Figure 6. An adaptive management project on the Colorado River focuses on the impacts of alternative low-flow releases through Glen Canyon Dam on ecological conditions in Grand Canyon National Park.

Earlier, we noted that traditional planning models and management organizations increasingly are subject to criticism as lacking a capacity (in terms of underlying philosophy as well as structure and process) to facilitate what is commonly defined as ecosystem management. Table 2 contrasts the qualities of two perspectives. It suggests that the underlying operational assumptions, organizational structure, and methods of operation of the alternatives stand in stark contrast. In particular, the traditional model is predicated on a world characterized by clarity in problem definition; on the ability to resolve problems through scientific, rational, quantitative, and objective means; and on a strong sense of order. In short, it is a model firmly grounded in the social reform planning tradition (Friedmann 1987).

Table 2. Traditional resource management versus ecosystem management

	Traditional management	Ecosystem management
Nature	To be dominated and mastered	Complex, changing, interrelated
Ethics	Compartmentalized; interrelationships marginal	Holistic, interrelationships important
Science and models	Deterministic, linear, static, steady-state equilibrium	Stochastic, nonlinear, dynamic, variable-rate dynamics, with temporary equilibria upset periodically by chaotic moments that set the stage for the next temporary equilibrium
	Robust, well-defined theory; discrete data and highly predictable outcomes	Embryonic, beginnings of theory, theory and practice intertwined, interrelated data, and unreliable outcomes
	Maps, linear optimization, monetized cost-benefit analysis, quantitative	Geographic information systems, relational databases, nonlinear simulation (time and space dependent), quantitative and qualitative evaluation for social, economic, and political aspects
Management and organization	Centralized, rigid; little focus on incentives or innovation	Decentralized, interrelated teams, adaptive, flexible; focus on incentives, innovation, shared learning
	Hierarchical, top-down bureaucracy	Adaptive, bottom-up, cooperative, open
Planning	Comprehensive, rational	Interrelated, chaotic, looking for order in chaos, imaginative
Decision making	Rigid, command-and-control, authoritarian, expert-driven	Deliberated, inclusive
	Science provides "the answers"	Science provides information; alone, it cannot provide answers Adapted to context of problems, interrelated to other problems, considers externalities
Participation	Influence, money	Discursive, deliberative
Leadership	Authoritarian, leaders designated	Situational; leaders arise from the community when needed

Source: Cortner and Moote 1999: 38.

This does not discount the value of traditional planning models in natural resource management. Nonetheless, organizing effective management programs requires a critical review of existing structures and processes and their capacity to deal with the world around us. This world is dominated by complexity and uncertainty, and these qualities compromise the ability of many contemporary organizations to frame effective approaches, given imbedded norms of risk-aversion and resistance to change. Lee (1993: 85) has summarized the key institutional challenges that account for this reluctance.

Adaptive management conditions	Rigidities that complicate experimentation
There is a mandate to take action in the face of uncertainty.	Experimentation and learning are at most secondary objectives in large ecosystems. Experimentation that conflicts with primary objectives will often be pushed aside or not proposed.
Decisionmakers are aware they are experimenting.	Experimentation is an admission there may be no positive return. More generally, specifying hypotheses to be tested raises the risk of perceived failure.
Decisionmakers care about improving outcomes over biological time scales.	Costs of monitoring, controls, and replication are substantial and they will appear especially high at the outset when compared with the costs of unmonitored trial and error. Individual decisionmakers rarely stay in office over times of biological significance.
Preservation of pristine environments is no longer an option, and human intervention cannot produce desired outcomes predictably.	Remedial action crosses jurisdictional boundaries and requires coordinated implementation over long periods.
Resources are sufficient to ecosystem behavior.	Data collection is vulnerable to external disruptions, such as budget cutbacks, policy changes, and controversy. After changes in leadership, decisionmakers may not be familiar with the purposes and values of an experimental approach.
Theory, models, and field methods are available to estimate and infer ecosystem-scale behavior.	Interim results may create panic or a realization that the experimental design was faulty. More generally, experimental findings will suggest policy changes; controversial changes could disrupt the experimental program.
Hypotheses can be formulated.	Accumulating knowledge may shift perceptions of what is worth examining via large-scale experimentation. For this reason, both policy actors and experimenters must adjust the tradeoffs among experimental and other policy objectives during the implementation process.
Organizational culture encourages learning from experience.	Advocates of adaptive management are likely to be staff, who have professional incentives to appreciate a complex process and a career situation in which long-term learning can be beneficial. Where there is a tension between staff and policy leadership, experimentation can become the focus of an internal struggle for control.
There is sufficient stability to measure long-term outcomes; institutional patience is essential.	Stability is usually dependent on factors outside the control of experimenters and managers.

A useful framework for conceptualizing the decision making environment occupied by natural resource agencies is described by Thompson and Tuden (1987) and also used by Lee (1993, 1999). Thompson and Tuden argued that when organizations make choices, they face two issues. First, choices are based on understanding **causation**. Do we understand why things work and can we predict what will happen when action is taken? Although Shannon and Antypas (1997) characterized uncertainty along a continuum (from relative surety to the unknown), Thompson and Tuden provided a simplified scheme, asking whether there is agreement or disagreement (figure 7).

Second, choices involve the nature of agreement regarding **preferences about outcomes**. This is a goal-oriented dimension; Shannon and Antypas (1997) described this as ambiguity. A major challenge confronting society today is that there is no clear, unequivocal sense of social purpose or single, unified public interest (Schubert 1960). Rather, the world is composed of numerous, often contradictory demands, creating an ambiguous context within which decisionmakers operate.

Despite the limits of treating uncertainty (causation) and ambiguity (preference) as dichotomous variables, Thompson and Tuden's schematic helps frame an understanding of the institutional choices confronting organizations implementing adaptive approaches. Consider the following. In cell A of figure 7, agreement exists on both causation and preferred outcomes. Here, decisionmakers are faced with issues primarily of a technical or computational nature; as a result, decision making is routinized. Under such conditions, the most appropriate institutional structure is the bureaucracy, embodying specialists operating in a formal, hierarchical, and routinized environment.

In cell B, although there is accord on preference, disagreement exists about causation. For example, although there is considerable agreement about the importance of maintaining old-growth conditions in forests, there is considerable disagreement about **how** this can best be accomplished (e.g., different thinning strategies, role of fire). Here, organizations must rely on expert judgment to help guide the decision making process. Because of differences in problem perception and interpretations of the scientific evidence, the collective wisdom of the decision unit needs to be brought to bear on the problem. The decision making strategy is judgment by majority and the preferred institutional structure to facilitate such choices is the collegium. Castleberry et al. (1996) provided a useful example by describing how the use of expert opinion among a variety of stream ecologists helped establish instream flow requirements.

In cell C, the situation is opposite to that in cell B; here, agreement exists on causation, but not on preference. When conflict exists over goals, inevitably there will be winners and losers; some will find their goals satisfied, others will not. This presents decisionmakers with a world where the choice process is driven by bargaining and negotiation, where compromise (the art of politics) must be practiced. It also means that decisionmakers need to be aware of what interests and values are involved, and who those losers and winners are. Thus, it is important that decision making processes involve as wide a representation of the multiple interests involved as possible (the United States Congress would be an example).

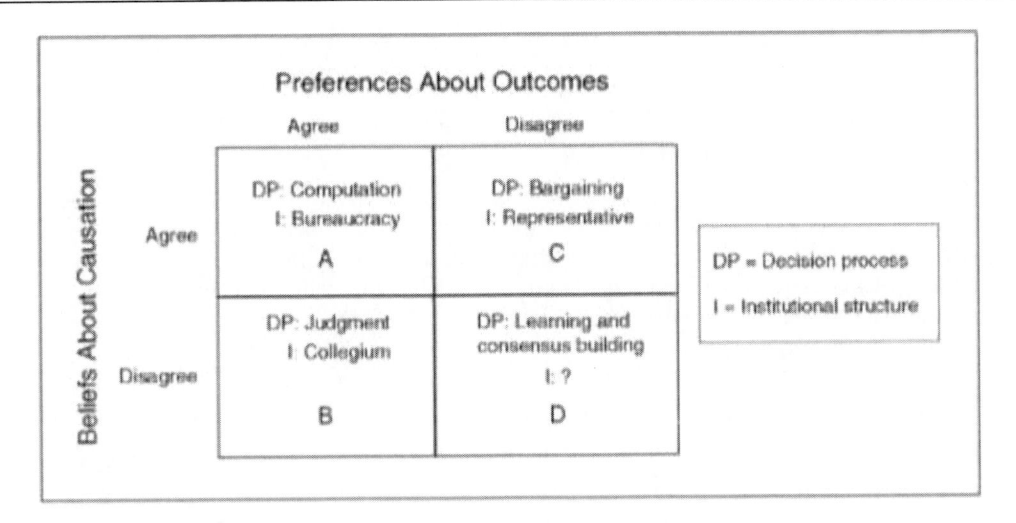

Figure 7. Thompson-Tuden model.

This brings us to the conditions that define cell D. Here, both causation and preference lack agreement; i.e., there are high levels of uncertainty and ambiguity. Thompson and Tuden described this as "a...dangerous situation for any group...; certainly by definition and probably in fact, the group...is nearing disintegration" (1987: 202).

Yet, this is a common situation today. For many resource managers, technical complexity, coupled with variation in natural processes, makes understanding causation problematic. Experts often disagree about what data mean, further confounding the exercise of informed decisions (Schwarz and Thompson 1990, Yankelovich 1991). In a pluralistic society, with high levels of political ambiguity, the search for preferred outcomes (e.g., some agreed-on purpose of public forests and forestry) faces formidable barriers. Fragmentation, intense political rivalries, and strategic posturing stymie efforts to find accord. Yet, despite this uncertainty and ambiguity, bureaucratic institutions, founded on the assumptions of certainty and clarity of purpose (the conditions of cell A), still dominate efforts to make choices. The result is a growing mismatch between current institutional structures and processes and the character of the decision environment within which those institutions operate.

However, "if not a bureaucracy, then what?" Thompson and Tuden described the context implied by cell D as one in which there is a state of anomie, of norm-lessness, where former goals and values have lost their meaning. But the search for appropriate institutional structures and processes capable of operating in such an environment reveals little of promise. Thompson and Tuden could only recommend a "structure for inspiration," an institution in which a charismatic leader offers a new set of ideals or preferences that "rally unity out of diversity" (1987: 202).

Lee (1993: 108) offered "two conceptually distinct strategies for intervening in a conflict (i.e., the conditions of cell D): either attempting to move toward agreement on causation, leaving preferences to be reconciled later; or attempting to move first on preferences." The second strategy involves consensus-building; contending parties strive to turn some initial consensus of goals into a plan to which all can agree. In short, he suggests through **planning** that it is possible to convert cell D conditions to those of cell B, where there is goal agreement. Alternatively, contesting parties strive to

> alter the character of the dispute by obtaining agreement on causation...This intervention method may be called **settling**, since the aim of the negotiation is not to achieve final resolution of conflict, but rather to hammer out joint actions within a relationship in which all parties are aware of and retain opposed interests...The reason parties...try to work together is that they have to (Lee 1993: 108–109).

In both cases, rather than developing a specific strategy for operating in the cell D domain, efforts are made to reframe the basic problem so that it fits elsewhere where decision processes and institutions are available.

Roe (1998) objected to Thompson and Tuden's conclusion, arguing there is something "which sticks in the throat" (p. 3) about hoping for revitalized institutions dependent on the appearance of inspirational, charismatic leaders. Rather than rejecting analysis, he argues that analysis remains the only viable option. What requires reassessment is the manner in which analysis is undertaken; "The analytic methods required for these sometimes desperate situations are...not those taught in most of our method courses and seminars...yet we proceed ahead today as if the old methods will get us across this complex public policy terrain" (Roe 1998: 4). The distinguishing characteristic of a more useful analytical approach is one that triangulates; i.e., that uses multiple methods, procedures, or theories to gain insight as to appropriate responses to complex policy questions. It also implies that multiple forms of governance might be required; traditional hierarchical/bureaucratic (command-and- control) systems, market-based systems, local self-governance. This would facilitate creation of a diverse set of decision rules affecting incentives, information flow, and compliance that would enhance the capacity to operate effectively in this turbulent domain (Dietz et al. 2003). On the other hand, the diversity of rules, structures, and processes might result in confusion and chaos that exacerbates turbulent conditions.

The challenge of finding institutional structures and processes capable of operating effectively in a world of uncertainty and ambiguity is formidable. Johnson and Williams (1999: 10) argued "...unresolved value judgments, and the lack of effective institutional structures for organizing debate...present the great threat to adaptive... management as a viable means for coping with...uncertainty." Yet, the literature contains important insight as to the desirable attributes such a structure might possess. Many of these qualities are consistent with the vision of adaptive management outlined in FEMAT.

Could adaptive management represent the kind of innovative strategy for more effectively operating in the ambiguity and uncertainty of a cell D world? It is probably not possible to answer the question definitively at this time, but the potential is there nonetheless. From a social and political perspective, adaptive management offers an opportunity for a more collaborative, multiparty and multi-interest approach, beginning at the problem-framing stage and extending through monitoring and evaluation. From a technical perspective, it offers the experimental foundation needed to operate more effectively relative to uncertainty and provides a means by which action can take place in the absence of a full understanding of consequences and implications.

Operational-level problems derive from inadequate or inappropriate organization of economic and public affairs and manifest themselves as ineffective management programs, insufficient or flawed information, inadequate legal processes, poorly-defined standards, etc. As Caldwell (1990: 72) noted, "the objective at this level is to rectify behavior without attempting to alter prevailing economic or institutional arrangements." In response to such problems, managerial organizations employ a variety of mechanisms designed to enhance efficiency: increasing incisive internal action, exercising increased control over what goes in and out of the organization, or strengthening management supervision and oversight (Michael 1973).

Because the nature of problems confronting organizations (of whatever structure) are systemic rather than operational, the required changes similarly must be systemic. Systemic environmental problems result from the underlying assumptions, goals, and values of modern technological and economic systems and priorities. Effective solutions must be similarly framed; adding another decimal point to the data or writing a new standard and guideline is inadequate to deal with the underlying causes of such problems. Rather, Caldwell (1990: 73) wrote, "the remedy (to systemic problem resolution) is sought in progressive adaptation and innovation in institutional arrangements."

Costanza et al. (2000: 153) identified several principles of governance around which a reconstituted organization capable of responding to complex environmental challenges might be built. These include:

1. **Responsibility**—Access to environmental resources carries attendant responsibilities.
2. **Scale-matching**—Institutions match the scale of the environmental problem.
3. **Precaution**—In the face of uncertainty about irreversible environmental impacts, humans should err on the side of caution.
4. **Adaptive management**—Decisionmakers acknowledge uncertainty and continuously gather and integrate information, with the goal of adaptive improvement.
5. **Full-cost allocation**—All internal and external costs and benefits of resource use are identified and appropriately allocated.
6. **Participation**—All affected stakeholders are engaged in the formulation and implementation of decisions concerning environmental resources.

These principles are consistent with attributes for effective environmental administration suggested by Paehlke and Torgerson (1990):

1. **Non-compartmentalized**—Organizations should resist the "bureaucratic tendency toward compartmentalization" (p. 292) and develop the capacity to embrace diverse disciplines as well as affected authorities.
2. **Open**—Institutional decision making is open and transparent. Given citizen access through legal processes as well as access to information through electronic means, the ability of organizations to bound debate and discussion within bureaucratic walls is unlikely.
3. **Decentralized**—Environmental management focuses on local, idiosyncratic issues. It must be sensitive to, and aware of, local knowledge and initiative, but also

acknowledge external factors and large-scale processes. The resulting "paradox of scale" (Lee and Stankey 1992: 35) places responsibility for ecological regulation in small-scale institutions, while locating coordinating responsibilities in collaborative structures at the ecological scale of the regulated system.

4. **Anti-technocratic**—Although scientific understanding is necessary for environmental administration, it is insufficient for handling environmental problems. Organizational processes must be conducted in a manner that educates both citizens and experts.
5. **Flexible**—The emergent quality of many environmental problems necessitates development of an adaptive capacity and an ability to operate under uncertainty and ambiguity.

Dietz et al. (2003) also examined the conditions necessary to foster what they described as "adaptive governance," a term selected to help convey the difficulty of control, the need to proceed in the face of uncertainty, and the importance of dealing effectively with diverse values, perspectives, and knowledge. They suggested that the requirements for operating in such a context include the provision of knowledge, a capacity to deal with conflict, developing strategies to induce compliance with rules, providing infrastructure, and fostering a capacity to operate in the face of change.

Collectively, the principles and concepts contained in these analyses (and others; see Dietz et al. 2003) lead to two basic conclusions. First, although various concepts have been posited in the literature, there is a growing consensus on the attributes institutions need to operate effectively in today's complex and uncertain environment. Second, the nature of effective institutions defies pressures for standardized models; Dovers and Mobbs (1997) suggested the precise nature of institutions capable of implementing adaptive management will always be a function of a particular context. Indeed, there is evidence that institutional diversity might prove as important as biological diversity for long-term survival (Ostrom et al. 1999). It is also apparent that institutions must be able to change (i.e., adapt) as the larger social and ecological context within which they exist change; Andries et al. (2004) have argued that this adaptive capacity within institutions is essential to ensuring their effectiveness.

However relevant the kinds of changes discussed above might appear, they also constitute changes in traditional natural resource management culture and beliefs (table 2) and in the relationship between management organizations and the public. Therefore, efforts to change likely will face resistance. Danter et al. (2000: 539) noted, "making such organizational changes creates significant changes in agency values and culture." Such values and the culture of natural resource management are deeply ingrained; collectively, they form a belief system highly resistant to change. But as we confront the issue of how best to facilitate adaptive management, we need to recognize that adaptive mechanisms, structures, and processes—qualities that often stand in sharp contrast to traditional management—are required (Grumbine 1997). It also means an increased capacity for learning must be present.

Michael (1995) described nine attributes of a learning organization:

1. **The organization understands that language impacts understanding.** Language can be a barrier (it discourages understanding and learning) or bridge (it facilitates

understanding and learning). People concerned with adaptive management need to pay attention to how we express ourselves and learn the language of **others.**

2. **Organizations operate on fundamental premises and assumptions about the world.** Both the Bureau of Land Management and Forest Service define themselves as problem-solving organizations. Such a belief can be used to act adaptively; these ideas serve as the basis for valuing learning.
3. **Such organizations explicitly acknowledge that the world is uncertain and that they need to accept error**. Typically, errors are treated as evidence of incompetence, miscalculation, and failure (Michael 1973). People who make errors, it follows, should be punished lest they become indifferent. Such a belief discourages the search for new knowledge—for thinking and acting adaptively—because such efforts often result in errors. Harvey (1988: 59) wrote "when we make it difficult for organization members to acknowledge their mistakes and have them forgiven, we have designed organizations that reduce risk taking, encourage lying, foment distrust, and, as a consequence, decrease productivity." Learning organizations operate in contrast to this.
4. **Learning organizations actively work to reduce the individual's fear of failure**. If error is inevitable, and if people associate such an outcome with sanctions and punishment, it is not surprising that risk-taking, innovation, and creativity suffer. Learning organizations explicitly acknowledge these fears and recognize concerns about power, status, and security. This makes it possible to discuss them openly, to deal with them positively, and to build intra-organizational trust. Lacking such acknowledgement, there will always be distrust and fear of others (e.g., they'll use new knowledge to their advantage and my disadvantage), thereby discouraging learning.
5. **Learning needs facilitators, not chairpersons.** Group and organizational learning requires guidance and a capacity to recognize and productively respond to subtle motives and behaviors that play out in any group. Direction from leaders often suppresses, rather than facilitates, learning.
6. **Learning organizations recognize the importance of training people in group process skills.** "Learning to learn depends on...skills that enhance task group behavior...(and)...is a necessary prelude to other types of learning in which persons must work together" (Michael 1995: 480-481). Providing constructive feedback, reflective thinking (Schön 1983), and joining are teachable abilities and are necessary in learning organizations.
7. **Learning organizations provide short-term reinforcements and rewards**. Generally, people react positively to rewards and recognition. This is important both in and outside the organization. In the Applegate AMA, for example, we find examples of the beneficial role of positive feedback from the community for agency staff (Rolle 2002). Rewards and reinforcements are essential to sustain a learning environment.
8. **We learn best when we educate others**. Teaching requires that one possess a comprehensive grasp of the topic. It also requires recognition that teaching means more than imparting knowledge to others; it involves the reciprocal processes of listening, processing, and evaluating. Learning organizations view members as educators (figure 8).

9. **Crises can be opportunities for learning**. Typically, organizations view their mission as one of preventing crises from occurring (Wildavsky 1988). However, crises are an inevitable part of the ecological processes around us, making the idea of prevention and control of such forces an illusion (Holling 1995). Such occurrences are opportunities for learning, and learning organizations capitalize on them by asking "How might we respond differently if we had the opportunity? Why did this event occur? or "What functions does it play?"

Danter et al. (2000) provided an example of the challenges facing the U.S. Fish and Wildlife Service (FWS) as it grappled with implementation of ecosystem management. They described four key areas facing the agency: (1) shifts in professional emphasis, (2) interdisciplinary collaboration, (3) the role of decision making , and (4) organizational values and culture.

Professional emphasis was shifting from stable, linear, and largely internal processes to constantly changing, nonlinear, and external pressures, conditions deemed largely outside the experience of most agency personnel. Demands for interdisciplinary collaboration were also stressful, as the bureaucratic structure, organized along compartmentalized, disciplinary boundaries, and exercising considerable control (at least in theory), was challenged to not only share (coordinate) information with external interests, but actually work collaboratively. Danter et al. (2000: 539) argued this shift from specialized and compartmentalized expertise to an interdisciplinary focus requires a "fundamental transformation of agency culture, power relationships, and professional norms." Decision making , undertaken with the expectation that it would facilitate an increase in predictability and a reduction in surprise, was forced to recognize the inevitable provisional nature of knowledge and the need for ongoing, adaptive management. Finally, traditional agency values and culture, featuring top-down control and communication, a concern with efficiency, and the bureaucratic organization itself were challenged.

Gary Wilson, USDA Natural Resources Conservation Service.

Figure 8. Learning involves more than acquiring more facts. It occurs best when there is a reciprocal process in which individuals listen, process, and evaluate information from one another. In this sense, effective learning organizations treat everyone as educators.

Danter et al. (2000: 540) concluded "ecosystem management itself requires transformational leadership after implementation because of the adaptive, nonlinear nature of ecosystem management." Although leadership is often defined in a bureaucratic and hierarchical manner, it is more appropriately seen as processes that establish direction, align people, and motivate and inspire—with the goal of producing change (Kotter 1995, Stankey et al. 2003a). Leadership, as opposed to management skills, among upper-and mid-level FWS officials, was the critical attribute in making the transition from a traditional management paradigm to ecosystem management as well as in maintaining an ongoing capacity to sustain that change. Danter et al. (2000: 544) noted:

> Ecosystem management demands continuous agency change, in that stable, linear, and predictable organizational processes will be replaced by adhocracy. For this reason, **after** implementation of ecosystem management, agency governance must be **more** leadership oriented than was previously required under earlier resource management models [emphases added].

The literature confirms the view of many observers that the major challenge facing adaptive management is fundamentally institutional in character. Such institutions are built on major premises and beliefs deeply imbedded in educational systems, laws, policies, and norms of professional behavior (Miller 1999). Although easy to say, institutional change is hard to do; Wilkinson (1992) described how the "lords of yesterday"—mining laws, timber and water resource development policies, and other natural resource laws and policies—framed a century ago, persist today, despite widespread recognition of the need for change.

Summary and Conclusion

In summary, what can be drawn from this extensive literature on adaptive management? In some cases, findings seem marked by consistency, whereas for others, the results are mixed or inconclusive. Yet, there are discernable patterns that foster efforts to assess the performance of adaptive management in the plan and the steps needed to increase its effectiveness.

1. **Although the concept of adaptive management is widely acclaimed in the literature as a model for resource management under conditions of risk and uncertainty, it remains primarily an ideal rather than a demonstrated reality.** In a review of bioregional assessments, Johnson and Herring (1999: 361) concluded "adaptive management is more of an abstraction than an acceptable enterprise, and institutions still do not allow managers to risk failure." Similarly, Lee (1999: 2) concluded "adaptive management has been much more influential as an idea than as a way of doing conservation." Although ideas are important and can serve as the basis for change and innovation, major challenges remain in translating adaptive management from rhetoric to reality. An important first step is to acknowledge that much remains to be done and that past experiences in incremental adjustments in light of new information typically do not meet the rigorous standards implied by contemporary notions of adaptive management.

2. **There are many definitions of adaptive management. Often, the term includes any process in which incremental adjustments occur. Typically, however, these do not involve the core characteristics of an adaptive approach as envisioned in the Plan or as discussed in the contemporary literature.** Although organizations long have relied on past experiences as a source of information to change subsequent policies and actions, such efforts generally lack the explicit hypothesis testing, monitoring, and evaluation that characterize contemporary definitions of adaptive management. In essence, adaptive management, as a process to accelerate and enhance learning based on the results of policy implementation, mimics the scientific method. Successful implementation of experimentally driven adaptive management requires incorporation of these distinctive characteristics, as opposed to simply a continuation of learning by incrementalism and trial and error. As Van Cleve et al. (2003: 21) noted "adaptive management is a very powerful, yet poorly understood natural resource management tool…but (it) must be understood by those who use, support, fund, and challenge it." Adaptive management, as described in the contemporary literature, is not simply the latest term embracing ad hoc or laissez faire management (MacKay et al. 2003). However, the literature reports few examples of formal structures and processes for implementing adaptive management. In the worst case, adaptive management has become a code phrase for "we'll make it up as we go." One unfortunate outcome of these disparate conceptions is that they confound efforts to undertake a comprehensive appraisal and evaluation of progress in implementing adaptive management.
3. **Experimentation is the core of adaptive management, involving hypotheses, controls, and replication**. Although adaptive management invites experiments involving tests of alternative resource management policies and institutional arrangements, it is rare to find examples of such experiments, particularly involving controls and replication. Such characteristics are difficult to impose in the complex, multijurisdictional settings commonly found at the landscape level. However, there has been a reluctance or even resistance to experimenting with alternative institutional structures and processes, such as integrating local knowledge into decision making processes.
4. **Adaptive management requires explicit designs that specify problem-framing and problem-solving processes, documentation and monitoring protocols, roles, relationships, and responsibilities, and assessment and evaluation processes**. This suggests that various ways to implement adaptive approaches exist, differing by context, organizational capacity, resources, etc. Unfortunately, clear documentation describing details of the experimentation process often fails to be undertaken, thereby diminishing the potential for feedback and learning. Guidelines and protocols to aid managers and policymakers in fashioning useful adaptive management models generally are lacking (an exception to this is Salafsky et al. 2001).
5. **Adaptive management is irreducibly sociopolitical in nature**. Effective implementation must involve the active involvement and support of the full set of partners and stakeholders. An inclusive approach is required not only to build understanding, support, credibility, and trust among constituent groups (Van Cleve et

al. 2003, MacKay et al. 2003), but also to ensure adequate problem-framing and access to the knowledge, experience, and skills held by these groups. Because natural resource management problems are social in origin and potential solutions are framed in a social context, effective management programs must embrace both biophysical and social elements. Agee (1999: 292) argued adaptive management can only work "if simultaneously adopted in the sociopolitical world" and although "the political world does not have to embrace uncertainty itself...it must fund activities that reduce or define uncertainty..." This has proven challenging because of the reluctance of parties to work collaboratively and because organizational and professional biases continue to define problems in technical, scientific terms (Miller 1999).

6. **An adaptive management approach is grounded in a recognition and acceptance of risk and uncertainty**. When working in a complex, chaotic, and contingent world characterized by imperfect knowledge and unpredictability, improved management and policymaking is dependent upon a learning process undertaken in a deliberate, thoughtful, and reflective manner (Buck et al. 2001). A key element of this is explicit acknowledgement and acceptance of the limits of understanding and the risks that accompany decisions undertaken in the face of such uncertainty. Yet, management organizations have been reluctant to do this; concerns with political and legal criticism and sanctions often lead to a denial of uncertainty and an unfounded confidence in the tentative, provisional nature of most policies (e.g., the S&Gs).
7. **Learning is a key output of the adaptive management process**. Learning can include improved technical knowledge regarding biophysical and socioeconomic systems and their interactions as well as greater insight as to how new understanding can be communicated, enhanced, and incorporated into organizational policies, programs, and procedures. Learning is driven by treating management policies as hypotheses and the resulting knowledge as input to subsequent actions. However, as Failing et al. (2004) have argued, the probability of acquiring useful information (i.e., learning) must be weighed against the likely impact of that information on decisions, and the costs incurred in acquiring that information. Adaptive management is both a good investment and an appropriate strategy when the probability of gaining useful information is high **and** the consequences of that information for pending decisions is also high. If the probability is high, but the consequences of information for decisions are low, there is a risk of investing scarce resources into a management strategy with a low probability of significant impact. In short, adaptive management is not always necessarily an appropriate strategy for proceeding in the face of uncertainty.
8. **Adaptive management focuses attention on the meaning and significance of learning**. Despite the importance of learning, it remains fundamentally inferential in nature; i.e., it must be inferred based on observations of behavior or communications that suggest learning. Parson and Clark (1995) suggested four questions to facilitate determination of whether learning has occurred: (1) Who or what learns; i.e., where does learning reside in an organization? (2) What kinds of things are learned; i.e., in terms of Ackoff's (1996) five dimensions of learning, does learning manifest itself as

more data, improved understanding, wisdom, etc.? (3) What counts as learning; i.e., does learning occur at the cognitive or behavioral level or both? What criteria, established through what processes, help identify whether the outcomes of an adaptive management approach constitute an adequate basis for changing or maintaining a policy or management strategy? (4) Why bother asking; i.e., are the results merely interesting or do they have consequences for organizational behavior?

9. **Effective adaptive management is open and responsive to varying forms and sources of knowledge**. This requires processes and structures that enable alternative forms of knowledge to be obtained and incorporated into the decision making process. Performance here is spotty, with public involvement venues and processes geared primarily to informing citizens of organizational intent or of obtaining some sense of public support or opposition to potential plans or policies.
10. **In the presence of risk and uncertainty, the adaptive management process provides a capacity to act in an informed, judicious manner**. This involves an acknowledgment that mistakes and failures are normal when working in uncertain situations, rather than unwanted feedback deriving from incompetence or inability (Schelhas et al. 2001). It highlights the importance of documentation, which provides a basis for examining differences between predicted and actual outcomes. All too often, negative outcomes are viewed as liabilities or even denied, rather than being seen as a source of learning and insight that could inform and improve subsequent decision making .
11. **A variety of institutional barriers confront effective implementation of adaptive management**. These include legal and political constraints (e.g., Endangered Species Act), socio-psychological barriers (e.g., risk-aversion; Miller 1999), and technical-scientific constraints (e.g., lack of adequate knowledge bases or appropriate monitoring protocols) (Stankey et al. 2003a). McLain and Lee (1996: 446) noted that "the adaptive management literature pays little attention to the question of what types of institutional structures and processes are required for the approach to work on a large-scale basis." There clearly is no single template or model most suited to an adaptive approach. However, the literature identifies several qualities that would characterize an adaptive institution; an atmosphere that is open, participatory and inclusive, integrative, collaborative, risk tolerant, and flexible. The search for design principles upon which adaptive institutions are founded will continue to draw attention (Andries et al. 2004). Ultimately, however, decisions about appropriate institutional structures and processes are linked to the specific context within which an adaptive approach is being considered.
12. **Effective implementation of adaptive management requires organizational leadership and political support, coupled with skilled advocates and champions at the field level**. A sustained commitment to adaptive management requires leadership and ongoing capacity-building efforts by organizations. Such commitment must be present at all organizational levels. Creation of the AMA coordinators and lead scientists was an important action in efforts to implement an adaptive approach in the Plan, and the loss of organizational commitment and support for these positions seriously constrains the future of adaptive management in the Plan.

13. **A commitment to adaptive management requires transition strategies that enable the transformation from a command-control system to one built upon learning, collaboration, and integrative management**. Ongoing assessments of needed changes in organizational structures and processes are essential. However, strong legal, organizational, and psychosocial forces work to sustain the status quo and resist efforts to change (Miller 1999). The ability of agencies to implement the systemic changes required in reframing existing conceptions of resource management—the role of citizens, managers, and scientists, the reality of dealing with a world characterized by chaos, complexity, and uncertainty, rather than order and predictability, etc.—remains problematic. Yet, as Holling (2004) has argued, transformational learning is necessary to enable truly novel strategies and processes to take root. Although such changes are inherently uncertain and unpredictable, they are essential to creating and sustaining the innovative environment within which an adaptive approach can successfully operate.

Implementing successful structures and processes to support adaptive management and the transitions through which organizational members must pass are formidable but essential. What is involved here is a need for **transformation**, a process with which the private and corporate sectors are well-acquainted (Blumenthal and Haspeslagh 1994, Holling 2004, Kotter 1995). These transformations often involve tensions among competing interests both internal and external to the organization. Bridges (1991) defined change as an objective and observable state that differs from the way things previously were. But the potential effectiveness of a change depends on the way individuals in the organization work through the **transition** from one state of conditions to another.

Transition is a psychological process; it begins with an ending. Traditional ways of operating within the organization have changed and members must come to grips with that fact. This is never easy, but it is an essential first step. Bridges (1991: 4) noted "nothing so undermines organizational change as the failure to think through who will have to let go of what when change occurs." Bridges described the second step in transition as negotiating through the neutral zone, a time and place of instability, ambiguity, and uncertainty. This can be threatening. What used to work no longer does; the rules that used to apply no longer fit. During this period, "anxiety rises and motivation falls," polarization among people increases, and the organization can become vulnerable to outside attack (Bridges 1991: 35–36). But it is also a creative period. Because old ways no longer work, there is a need to find new ways that do, and these provide organizational members with opportunities for creativity, innovation, and reinvention. Finally, the third step involves arrival at a new state of affairs. And the cycle begins again.

Although barriers continue to face implementation of adaptive management, the concept remains an important, even essential, component of efforts to deal more effectively with today's complex, uncertain world. In the absence of an adaptive grounded approach, rule-based planning—administrative or legal—will continue to dominate management, with a further diminution of the ability of managers to modify actions and policies in light of new knowledge and experience. To avoid this will call for renewed innovation and leadership from all interested parties: managers, policymakers, scientists, and citizens.

REFERENCES

Ackoff, R. L. (1996). On learning and the systems that facilitate it. *Reflections*, *1*(1), 14–24.

Agee, J. K. (1999). Science review. In: Johnson, K.N.; Swanson, F.; Herring, M.; Greene, S., eds. Bioregional assessments: science at the crossroads of management and policy. Washington, DC: Island Press, 288–292.

Allan, C. & Curtis, A. (2003). Regional scale adaptive management: lessons from the North East Salinity Strategy (NESS). *Australasian Journal of Environmental Management*, 10(June), 76–84.

Allen, G. M. & Gould, E. M. Jr. (1986). Complexity, wickedness, and public forests. *Journal of Forestry*, *84*(4), 20–23.

Allenby, B. R. & Richards, D. J. (1994). The greening of industrial ecosystems. Washington, DC: National Academy Press. 259 p.

Andries, J. M., Janssen, M. A. & Ostrom, E. (2004). A framework to analyze the robustness of social-ecological systems from an institutional perspective. *Ecology and Society*, *9*(1), 18. http://www.ecologyandsociety.org/vol9/iss1/138. (June 17, 2004).

Argyris, C. & Schön, D. (1978). Organization learning: a theory of action perspective. Reading, MA: Addison-Wesley. 344 p.

Ashworth, M. J. (1982). Feedback design of systems with significant uncertainty. Chichester, UK: Research Studies Press. 246 p.

Bardwell, L. V. (1991). Problem-framing: a perspective on environmental problem- solving. *Environmental Management*, *15*(5), 603–612.

Bednar, L. F. & Shainsky, L. J. (1996). The concept of overcontrolled systems: implications for forest management. *Journal of Forestry*, *94*(8), 29–33.

Bernstein, B. B. & Zalinski, J. (1986). A philosophy for effective monitoring. In: Oceans 86 monitoring strategies symposium. Washington, DC: Marine Technology Society, 1024–1029. Vol. *3*.

Blumenthal, B. & Haspeslagh, P. (1994). Toward definition of corporate transformation. *Sloan Management Review*, *35*(3), 101–106.

Bormann, B. T., Brookes, M. H., Ford, E. D., Kiester, A. R., Oliver, C. D. & Weigand, J. F. (1994a). Volume 5: a framework for sustainable-ecosystem management. Gen. Tech. Rep. PNW-GTR-331. Portland, OR: U.S. Department of Agriculture, Forest Service, Pacific Northwest Research Station. 61 p.

Bormann, B. T., Cunningham, P. G., Brookes, M. H., Manning, V. W. & Collopy, M. W. (1994b). Adaptive ecosystem management in the Pacific Northwest. Gen. Tech. Rep. PNW-GTR-341. Portland, OR: U.S. Department of Agriculture, Forest Service, Pacific Northwest Research Station. 22 p.

Bormann, B. T., Martin, J. R., Wagner, F. H., Wood, G. W., Alegria, J., Cunningham, P. G., Brookes, M. H., Friesema, P., Berg, J. & Henshaw, J. R. (1999). Adaptive management. In: Johnson, N.C.; Malk, A.J.; Sexton, W.T.; Szaro, R., eds. Ecological stewardship: a common reference for ecosystem management. Oxford, United Kingdom: Elsevier Science Ltd., 505-534, Vol. *3*.

Bridges, W. (1991). Managing transitions: making the most of change. Reading, MA: Addison-Wesley Publishing Co. 130 p.

British Columbia Ministry of Forests. (2000). Single and double loop learning. *Adaptive Management Newsletter*. Summer: 1–2.

Buck, L. E., Geisler, C. C., Schelhas, J., Wollenberg, E., eds. (2001). Biological diversity: balancing interests through adaptive collaborative management. New York: CRC Press. 465 p.

Butler, M. J., Steele, L. L. & Robertson, R. A. (2001). Adaptive resource management in the New England groundfish fishery: implications for public participation and impact assessment. *Society and Natural Resources*, *14*(9), 791–801.

Buttolph, L. P. & Doak, S. C. (2000). The integration of knowledge in place-based ecosystem management. Report to the People and Natural Resources Program. Portland, OR: Ecotrust. 51 p.

Caldwell, L. K. (1990). Between two worlds: science, the environmental movement, and policy choice. Cambridge, United Kingdom: Cambridge University Press. 224 p.

Castleberry, D. T., Cech, J. J. Jr., Erman, D. C., Hankin, D., Healey, M., Kondolf, G. M., Mangel, M., Mohr, M., Moyle, P. B., Nielsen, J., Speed, T. P. & Williams, J. G. (1996). Uncertainty and instream flow standards. *Fisheries*, *21*(8), 20–21.

Clayton, A. M. H. & Radcliffe, N. J. (1996). *Sustainability: a systems approach*. Boulder, CO: Westview Press. 258 p.

Cortner, H. J. & Moote, M. A. (1999). *The politics of ecosystem management*. Washington, DC: Island Press. 179 p.

Cortner, H. J., Shannon, M. A., Wallace, M. G., Burke, S. & Moote, M. A. (1996). Institutional barriers and incentives for ecosystem management: a problem analysis. Gen. Tech. Rep. PNW-GTR-354. Portland, OR: U.S. Department of Agriculture, Forest Service, Pacific Northwest Research Station. 35 p.

Costanza, R., Daly, H., Folke, C., Hawken, P., Holling, C. S., McMichael, A. J., Pimentel, D. & Rapport, D. (2000). Managing our environmental portfolio. *BioScience*, *50*(2), 149–155.

Danter, K. J., Briest, D. L., Mullins, G. W. & Norland, E. (2000). Organizational change as a component of ecosystem management. *Society and Natural Resources*, *13*(6), 537–547.

Dietz, T., Dolšak, N., Ostrom, E. & Stern, P. C. (2003). The drama of the commons. In: Ostrom, E.; Dietz, T.; Dolšak, N.; Stern, P.C.; Stonich, S.; Weber, E.U., eds. The drama of the commons. Washington, DC: National Academy Press: 3–35.

Dovers, S. (2003). Processes and institutions for environmental management: why and how to analyse. In: Dovers, S.; River, S.W., eds. Managing Australia's environment. Sydney, Australia: The Federation Press: 3–12.

Dovers, S. R. & Mobbs, C. D. (1997). An alluring prospect? Ecology, and the requirements of adaptive management. In: Klomp, N.; Lunt, I., eds. Frontiers in ecology: building the links. Oxford, United Kingdom: Elsevier Science Ltd., 39–52.

Dryzek, J. S. (1987). Rational ecology. New York: Basil Blackwell, Inc. 270 p.

Duinker, P. N. & Trevisan, L. M. (2003). Adaptive management: progress and prospects for Canadian forests. In: Burton, P.J.; Messier, C.; Smith, D.W.; Adamowicz, W.L., eds. Towards sustainable management of the boreal forest. Ottawa, Ontario: NRC Research Press: 857–892.

Easterby-Smith, M. & Araujo, M. L. (1999). Organizational learning: current debates and opportunities. In: Easterby-Smith, M.; Burgoyne, J.; Araujo, M.L., eds. Organizational learning and the learning organization: developments in theory and practice. London: Sage Publications: 2–21.

Environmental and Social Systems Analysts, Ltd. [ESSA]. (1982). Review and evaluation of adaptive environmental assessment and management. Ottawa, ON: Environment Canada. 116 p.

Estill, E. (1999). Blazing trails in the Forest Service: ecosystem management and social science. In: Cordell, H.K.; Bergstrom, J.C., eds. Integrating social sciences with ecosystem management. Champaign, IL: Sagamore Press: 13–23.

Ewing, S. A., Grayson, R. B. & Argent, R. M. (2000). Science, citizens, and catchments: decision support for catchment planning in Australia. *Society and Natural Resources, 13*(5), 443–459.

Failing, E., Horn, G. & Higgins, P. (2004). Using expert judgment and stakeholder values to evaluate adaptive management options. *Ecology and Society, 9*(1), 13. http://www.ecologyandsociety.org/vol9/iss1/13. (June 17, 2004).

Falanruw, M. V. C. (1984). People pressure and management of limited resources on Yap. In: McNeely, J.A.; Miller, K.R., eds. National parks, conservation, and development: the role of protected areas in sustaining society. Washington, DC: The Smithsonian Institution Press: 348–354.

Forest Ecosystem Management Assessment Team [FEMAT]. (1993). An ecological, economic, and social assessment. Portland, OR: U.S. Department of Agriculture; U.S. Department of the Interior [et al.]. [Irregular pagination].

Friedmann, J. (1987). Planning in the public domain: from knowledge to action. Princeton, NJ: Princeton University Press. 501 p.

Gilmour, A., Walkerden, G. & Scandol, J. (1999). Adaptive management of the water cycle on the urban fringe: three Australian case studies. *Conservation Ecology, 3*(1), 11. http://www.consecol.org/vol3/iss1/art11. (May 17, 2001).

Gray, A. N. (2000). Adaptive ecosystem management in the Pacific Northwest: a case study from coastal Oregon. *Conservation Ecology, 4*(2), 6. http:///www.consecol. org/vol4/iss2/art6. (April 22, 2001).

Grumbine, R. E. (1997). Reflections on "What is ecosystem management?" *Conservation Biology, 11*(1), 41–47.

Gunderson, L. (1999a). Red queens to mad hatters—a wonderland of landscapes and institutions. In: Views from the ridge: considerations for planning at the landscape level. Portland, OR: U.S. Department of Agriculture, Forest Service, Pacific Northwest Research Station; Western Forestry and Conservation Association: 49–57.

Gunderson, L. (1999b). Resilience, flexibility and adaptive management—antidotes for spurious certitude? *Conservation Ecology, 3*(1), 7. http://www.consecol.org/vol3/iss1/art7. (January 12, (2000).

Gunderson, L. (1999c). Stepping back: assessing for understanding in complex regional systems. In: Johnson, K.N.; Swanson, F.; Herring, M.; Greene, S., eds. Bioregional assessments: science at the crossroads of management and policy. Washington, DC: Island Press: 27–40.

Gunderson, L. H., Holling, C. S., Light, S. S., eds. (1995a). Barriers and bridges to the renewal of ecosystems and institutions. New York: Columbia University Press. 593 p.

Gunderson, L. H., Holling, C. S. & Light, S. S. (1995b). Barriers broken and bridges built: a synthesis. In: Gunderson, L.H.; Holling, C.S.; Light, S.S., eds. Barriers and bridges to the renewal of ecosystems and institutions. New York: Columbia University Press: 489–532.

Gurvitch, G. (1971). The social frameworks of knowledge. Oxford, United Kingdom: Basil Blackwell. 292 p.

Haber, S. (1964). Efficiency and uplift: scientific management in the progressive era, 1890–1920. Chicago, IL: University of Chicago Press. 181 p.

Halbert, C. L. (1993). How adaptive is adaptive management? Implementing adaptive management in Washington state and British Columbia. *Reviews in Fisheries Science, 1*, 261–283.

Haney, A. & Power, R. L. (1996). Adaptive management for sound ecosystem management. *Environmental Management, 20*(6), 879–886.

Harvey, J. B. (1988). The Abilene paradox and other meditations on management. Lexington, MA: Lexington Books. 150 p.

Herrick, C. & Sarewitz, D. (2000). Ex post evaluation: a more effective role for scientific assessments in environmental policy. *Science, Technology, and Human Values, 25*(3), 309–331.

Hilborn, R. (1992). Institutional learning and spawning channels for sockeye salmon (*Oncorhynchus nerka*). *Canadian Journal of Fisheries and Aquatic Sciences, 49*, 1126–1136.

Holling, C. S. (1978). *Adaptive environmental assessment and management*. London: John Wiley. 377 p.

Holling, C. S. (1995). What barriers? What bridges? In: Gunderson, L.H.; Holling, C.S.; Light, S.S., eds. Barriers and bridges to the renewal of eco-systems and institutions. New York: Columbia University Press: 3–34.

Holling, C. S. (2004). From complex regions to complex worlds. *Ecology and Society, 9*(1), 11. http://www.ecologyandsociety.org/vol9/iss1/art11. (June 17, 2004).

Holzner, B. & Marx, J. H. (1979). Knowledge application: the knowledge system in society. Boston: Allyn and Bacon, Inc. 388 p.

Huber, P. (1983). The old-new division in risk regulation. *The Virginia Law Review, 69*(6), 1025–1107.

Inkpen, A. C. & Crossan, M. M. (1995). Believing is seeing: joint ventures and organizational learning. *Journal of Management Studies, 32*(5), 595–618.

Johnson, B. L. (1999). Introduction to the special issue: Adaptive management—scientifically sound, socially challenged? *Conservation Ecology, 3*(1), 8. http://www.consecol.org/vol3/iss1/art10. (January 4, 2000)

Johnson, K. N. & Herring, M. (1999). Understanding bioregional assessments. In: Johnson, K.N.; Swanson, F.; Herring, M.; Greene, S., eds. Bioregional assessments: science at the crossroads of management and policy. Washington, DC: Island Press: 341–376.

Johnson, F. & Williams, K. (1999). Protocol and practice in the adaptive management of waterfowl harvests. *Conservation Ecology, 3*(1), 8. http://www.consecol.org/vol3/iss1/art8. (January 7, 2000).

Kloppenburg, J. Jr. (1991). Social theory and the de/reconstruction of agricultural science: local knowledge for an alternative agriculture. *Rural Sociology, 56*, 519–548.

Korten, D. C., Klauss, R., eds. (1984). People-centered development: contributions toward theory and planning frameworks. Hartford, CT: Kumarian Press. 333 p.

Kotter, J. P. (1995). Leading change: why transformational efforts fail. *Harvard Business Review*. March-April: 59–67.

Kuhn, T. (1970). The structure of scientific revolutions. Chicago: University of Chicago Press. 210 p.

Kusel, J., Doak, S. C., Carpenter, S. & Sturtevant, V. E. (1996). The role of the public in adaptive ecosystem management. In: Sierra Nevada ecosystem project: final report to Congress. Vol. II, assessments and scientific basis for management options. Davis, CA: University of California, Centers for Water and Wildland Resources: 611–624.

Ladson, A. R. & Argent, R. M. (2002). Adaptive management of environmental flows: lessons for the Murray-Darling Basin from three large North American rivers. *Australian Journal of Water Resources*, *5*(1), 89–101.

Lang, R. (1990). Achieving integration in resource planning. In: Lang, R. (ed.), Integrated approaches to resource planning and management. Calgary, AB: University of Calgary, Banff Centre for Continuing Education: 27–50.

Lee, K. N. (1993). Compass and gyroscope: integrating science and politics for the environment. Washington, DC: Island Press. 243 p.

Lee, K. N. (1995). Deliberately seeking sustainability in the Columbia River basin. In: Gunderson, L.H.; Holling, C.S.; Light, S.S., eds. Barriers and bridges to the renewal of ecosystems and institutions. New York: Columbia University Press: 214–238.

Lee, K. N. (1999). Appraising adaptive management. *Conservation Ecology*, *3*(2), 3. http://www.consecol.org/vol3/iss2/art3. (January 4, 2000).

Lee, K. N. & Lawrence, J. (1986). Adaptive management: learning from the Columbia River basin fish and wildlife program. *Environmental Law*, *16*, 431–460.

Lee, R. G. & Stankey, G. H. (1992). Evaluating institutional arrangements for regulating large watersheds and river basins. In: Adams, P.W.; Atkinson, W.A., comps. Watershed resources: balancing environmental, social, political and economic factors in large basins. Corvallis, OR: Forest Engineering Department, Oregon State University: 30–37.

Levitt, B. & March, J. G. (1988). Organizational learning. *Annual Review of Sociology*, *14*, 319–340.

Lindblom, C. (1959). The science of muddling through. *Public Administration Review*, *19*(2), 79–99.

Lowe, I. (1990). Scientific objectivity and values. In: Webb, L.J.; Kikkawa, J., eds. Australian tropical forests: science—values—meaning. Melbourne, Victoria, Australia: Commonwealth Scientific and Industrial Research Organisation: 133–141.

Ludwig, D., Hilborn, R. & Walters, C. (1993). Uncertainty, resource exploitation, and conservation: lessons from history. *Science*, *260*, 17, 36.

MacKay, H. M., Rogers, K. H. & Roux, D. J. (2003). Implementing the South African water policy: holding the vision while exploring an uncharted mountain. *Water SA*, *29*(4), 353–358.

Mapstone, B. (2003). Institutional and objective certainty: obstacles to the implementation of active adaptive management. In: Allan, C.; Curtis, A., comps. *Notes from an adaptive management workshop*. Report 171. Albury, New South Wales, Australia: Johnstone Centre: 17–18.

Marcot, B. G. (1998). Selecting appropriate statistical procedures and asking the right questions: a synthesis. In: Sit, V.; Taylor, B., eds. Statistical methods for adaptive management studies. Victoria, BC: Ministry of Forests, Research Branch: 129–143.

Mazaika, R., Lackey, R. T., Friant, S. L., eds. (1995). Ecological risk assessment: use, abuse, and alternatives. *Human and Ecological Risk Assessment*, *1*(4), 337–458.

McCay, B. J. (2002). Emergence of institutions for the commons: contexts, situations, and events. In: Ostrom, E.; Dietz, T.; Dolšak, N.; Stern, P.C.; Stonich, S.; Weber, E.U., eds. The drama of the commons. Washington, DC: National Academy Press: 361–402.

McLain, R. J. & Lee, R. G. (1996). Adaptive management: promises and pitfalls. *Environmental Management*, *20*(4), 437–448.

Meppem, T. & Bellamy, J. (2003). Building capacity for adaptive management: experiences from two community based regional initiatives. In: Allan, C.; Curtis, A., comps. Notes from an adaptive management workshop. Rep. 171. Albury, New South Wales, Australia: Johnstone Centre: 15–16.

Mezirow, J. (1995). Transformation theory of adult learning. In: Welton, M.R., ed. In defense of the lifeworld: critical perspectives on adult learning. New York: State University of New York: 39–70.

M'Gonigle, R. M., Jamieson, T. L., McAllister, M. K. & Peterman, R. M. (1994). Taking uncertainty seriously: from permissive regulation to preventative design environmental decision making. *Osgoode Hall Law Journal*, *32*(1), 99–169.

Michael, D. N. (1973). On learning to plan—and planning to learn. San Francisco: Jossey-Bass Publishers. 341 p.

Michael, D. N. (1995). Barriers and bridges to learning in a turbulent human ecology. In: Gunderson, L.H.; Holling, C.S.; Light, S.S., eds. Barriers and bridges to the renewal of ecosystems and institutions. New York: Columbia University Press: 461–488.

Miller, A. (1993). The role of analytical science in natural resource decision making. *Environmental Management*, *17*(5), 563–574.

Miller, A. (1999). Environmental problem solving: psychosocial barriers to adaptive change. New York: Springer-Verlag. 239 p.

National Research Council. (1999). Downstream: adaptive management of Glen Canyon Dam and the Colorado River ecosystem. Washington, DC: National Academy Press. 230 p.

Nelson, J. E. (1999). Management review (of the FEMAT case study). In: Johnson, K.N.; Swanson, F.; Herring, M.; Greene, S., eds. Bioregional assessments: science at the crossroads of management and policy. Washington, DC: Island Press: 121–126.

Ostrom, E. (1986). An agenda for the study of institutions. *Public Choice*, *48*, 3–25.

Ostrom, E., Burger, J., Field, C. B., Norgaard, R. B. & Policansky, D. (1999). Revisiting the commons: local lessons, global challenges. *Science*, *284*, 278–282.

Paehlke, R. & Torgerson, D. (1990). Environmental politics and the administrative state. In: Paehlke, R.; Torgerson, D., eds. Managing leviathan: environmental politics and the administrative state. Peterborough, ON: Broadview Press: 285–301.

Pahl-Wostl, C. (1995). The dynamic nature of ecosystems: chaos and order entwined. Chichester, England: John Wiley & Sons. [Pages unknown].

Parson, E. A. & Clark, W. C. (1995). Sustainable development as social learning: theoretical perspectives and practical challenges for the design of a research program. In: Gunderson, L.H.; Holling, C.S.; Light, S.S., eds. Barriers and bridges to the renewal of ecosystems and institutions. New York: Columbia University Press: 428–460.

Perry, E. A. (1995). Salmon stock restoration and enhancement: strategies and experiences in British Columbia. *American Fisheries Society Symposium, 15*, 152–160.

Reichhardt, T. (1997). Endangered species bill faces battle against property lobby. *Nature, 307*, 321–326.

Renn, O. (1992). Concepts of risk: a classification. In: Krimsky, S.; Golding, D., eds. Social theories of risk. Westport, CT: Praeger Publishing: 53–82.

Roe, E. (1996). Why ecosystem management can't work without social science: an example from the California northern spotted owl controversy. *Environmental Management, 5*, 667–674.

Roe, E. (1998). Taking complexity seriously: policy analysis, triangulation and sustainable development. Boston: Kluwer Academic Publishers. 138 p.

Rolle, S. (2002). Measures of progress for collaboration: case study of the Applegate Partnership. Gen. Tech. Rep. PNW-GTR-565. Portland, OR: U.S. Department of Agriculture, Forest Service, Pacific Northwest Research Station. 13 p.

Saint-Onge, H. (1996). Tacit knowledge: the key to the strategic alignment of intellectual capital. *Strategy and Leadership, 24*(2), 10, 12–14.

Salafsky, N., Margoluis, R. & Redford, K. (2001). Adaptive management: a tool for conservation practitioners. Washington, DC: Biodiversity Support Program, World Wildlife Fund, Inc. 136 p. http://fosonline.org/resourcesAdapManHTML/ adman_1.html. (February 6, 2004).

Schelhas, J., Buck, L. E. & Geisler, C. C. (2001). Introduction: the challenge of adaptive collaborative management. In: Buck, L.E.; Geisler, C.C.; Schelhas, J.; Wollenberg, E., eds. Biological diversity: balancing interests through adaptive collaborative management. New York: CRC Press: xix-xxxv.

Schiff, A. L. (1962). Fire and water: scientific heresy in the Forest Service. Cambridge, MA: Harvard University Press: [Pages unknown].

Schön, D. A. (1983). The reflective practitioner: how professionals think in action. New York: Basic Books. 374 p.

Schubert, G. (1960). The public interest: a critique of the theory of a political concept. Glencoe IL: The Free Press of Glencoe. 244 p.

Schwarz, M. & Thompson, M. (1990). Divided we stand: redefining politics, technology and social choice. Philadelphia, PA: University of Pennsylvania Press. 176 p.

Senge, P. M. (1990). The fifth discipline: the art and practice of the learning organization. New York: Currency Doubleday. 423 p.

Shannon, M. A. (1987). Forest planning: learning with people. In: Miller, M.L.; Gale, R.P.; Brown, P.J., eds. Social science in natural resource management systems. Boulder, CO: Westview Press: 233–247.

Shannon, M. A. & Antypas, A. R. (1997). Open institutions: uncertainty and ambiguity in 21st-century forestry. In: Kohm, K.A.; Franklin, J.F., eds. Creating a forestry for the 21st century: the science of ecosystem management. Washington, DC: Island Press: 437–445.

Smith, C. L., Gilden, J., Steel, B. S. & Mrakovcich, K. (1998). Sailing the shoals of adaptive management: the case of salmon in the Pacific Northwest. *Environmental Management, 22*(5), 671–681.

Socolow, R. H. (1976). Failures of discourse: obstacles to the integration of environmental values into natural resource policy. In: Tribe, L.H.; Schelling, C.S.; Voss, J., eds. When values conflict: essays on environmental analysis, discourse, and decision. Cambridge, MA: Ballinger Company: 1–33.

Stankey, G. H., Bormann, B. T., Ryan, C., Shindler, B., Sturtevant, V., Clark, R. N. & Philpot, C. (2003a). Adaptive management and the Northwest Forest Plan: rhetoric and reality. *Journal of Forestry*, *101*(1), 40–46.

Stankey, G. H., McCool, S. F. & Clark, R. N. (2003b). Building innovative institutions for ecosystem management: integrating analysis and inspiration. In: Shindler, B.A.; Beckley, T.M.; Finley, M.C., eds. Two paths toward sustainable forests: public values in Canada and the United States. Corvallis, OR: Oregon State University Press: 271–295.

Stankey, G. H. & Shindler, B. (1997). Adaptive management areas: achieving the promise, avoiding the peril. Gen. Tech. Rep. PNW-GTR-394. Portland OR: U.S. Department of Agriculture, Forest Service, Pacific Northwest Research Station. 21 p.

Thomas, J. W. (1999). Learning from the past and moving to the future. In: Johnson, K.N.; Swanson, F.; Herring, M.; Greene, S., eds. Bioregional assessments: science at the crossroads of management and policy. Washington, DC: Island Press: 11–25.

Thompson, J. D. & Tuden, A. (1987). Strategies, structures, and processes of organizational decision. In: Thompson, J.D.; Hammond, P.B.; Hawkes, R.W.; Junker, B.H.; Tuden, A., eds. Comparative studies in administration. New York: Garland Publishing Company: 197–216.

Tsang, E. W. K. (1997). Organizational learning and the learning organization: a dichotomy between descriptive and prescriptive research. *Human Relations*, *50*(1), 73–89.

U.S. Department of Agriculture, Forest Service; U.S. Department of the Interior, Bureau of Land Management [USDA USDI]. (1994). Record of decision for amendments to Forest Service and Bureau of Land Management planning documents within the range of the northern spotted owl. [Place of publication unknown.] 74 p. [Plus attachment A: standards and guidelines].

Van Cleve, F. B., Simenstad, C., Goetz, F. & Mumford, T. (2003). Application of "best available science" in ecosystem restoration: lessons learned from large-scale restoration efforts in the U.S. Puget Sound Nearshore Ecosystem Restoration Project. 38 p. http://www.pugetsoundnearshore.org. [Date accessed unknown].

Volkman, J. M. & McConnaha, W. E. (1993). Through a glass, darkly: Columbia River salmon, the Endangered Species Act, and adaptive management. *Environmental Law*, *23*(4), 1249–1272.

Walters, C. J. (1986). Adaptive management of renewable resources. New York: Macmillan. 374 p.

Walters, C. J. (1997). Challenges in adaptive management of riparian and coastal ecosystems. *Conservation Ecology*, *1*(2), 1. http://www.consecol.org/vol1/iss2/ art1. (October 5, 1999).

Walters, C. J. & Holling, C. S. (1990). Large-scale management experiments and learning by doing. *Ecology*, *71*(6), 2060–2068.

Watkins, K. E. (1996). Individuals who learn create organizations that learn. In: Workplace learning: debating five critical questions of theory and practice. Directions for Adult and Continuing Education. San Francisco: Jossey-Bass. 72:(Winter): 89–96.

Weinberg, A. (1962). Science and trans-science. *Minerva*, *9*, 220–232.

Wildavsky, A. (1979). Speaking truth to power: the art and craft of policy analysis. Boston: Little, Brown, and Company. 431 p.

Wildavsky, A. (1988). Searching for safety. Bowling Green, OH: Social Philosophy and Policy Center and Transaction Publishers. 253 p.

Wilkinson, C. F. (1992). Crossing the next meridian: land, water, and the future of the West. Washington, DC: Island Press. 376 p.

Wilson, J. (2002). Scientific uncertainty, complex systems, and the design of common-pool institutions. In: Ostrom, E.; Dietz, T.; Dolšak, N.; Stern, P.C.; Stonich, S., Weber, E.U., eds. The drama of the commons. Washington, DC: National Academy Press: 327–359.

Wondolleck, J. M. (1988). Public lands conflict and resolution: managing national forest disputes. New York: Plenum Press. 263 p.

Yankelovich, D. (1991). Coming to public judgment: making democracy work in a complex world. Syracuse, NY: Syracuse University Press. 290 p.

Yorks, L. & Marsick, V. J. (2000). Organizational learning and transformation. In: Mezirow, J., ed. Learning as transformation: critical perspectives on a theory in progress. San Francisco: Jossey Bass Publishers: 253–281.

End Notes

[1] Stankey, G.H.; Bormann, B.T.; Ryan, C.; Shindler, B.; Sturtevant, V.; Clark, R.N.; Philpot, C., eds. Learning to manage a complex ecosystem: adaptive management and the Northwest Forest Plan. Draft manuscript on file with G.H. Stankey.

[2] "Models," as used in this report, include a variety of depictions intended to simplify complexity.

In: Adaptive Management of Natural Resources
Editor: Damian Lowell

ISBN: 978-1-63321-357-9

Chapter 2

ADAPTIVE MANAGEMENT: THE U.S. DEPARTMENT OF THE INTERIOR APPLICATIONS GUIDE*

Byron K. Williams and Eleanor D. Brown

EXECUTIVE SUMMARY

Our country's natural resource challenges today are more complex and more difficult to resolve than ever before. The loss of biodiversity, changing climatic patterns, spread of invasive species, alteration of landscapes, and many other problems pose serious threats to the long-term sustainability of America's natural resources. We urgently need to find new ways to address these problems. In particular, we need new methods and technologies to deal with the scale of the human footprint on the landscape, and new approaches to address the impacts of that footprint. A major challenge is to account for, and ultimately improve, our understanding of the long-term consequences of our actions.

For many important problems now facing resource managers and conservationists, adaptive management is a promising means of facilitating decision making and helping to resolve the uncertainties that hinder effective management. This applications guide builds on the framework of the DOI Adaptive Management Technical Guide (Williams et al. 2007), which describes adaptive management in terms of learning-based management of natural resources. In this guide, we use case studies to show how adaptive management can be used for both management and learning. We focus on practical applications in the areas of importance to DOI managers – climate change, water, energy, and human impacts on the landscape. We present adaptive management as a form of structured decision making, with an emphasis on the value of reducing uncertainty over time in order to improve management. The first half of the guide covers the foundations and challenges of adaptive management, and the second half documents examples that illustrate the components of adaptive management.

---

* This is an edited, reformatted and augmented version of a document released by the Adaptive Management Working Group, U.S. Department of the Interior, April 2012.

Framework of Adaptive Management

Adaptive management can be useful in cases where natural resources are responsive to management, but there is also uncertainty about the impacts of management interventions. Its origin is rooted in parallel concepts from a variety of perspectives, but in natural resources the term simply means learning by doing, and adapting based on what's learned (Walters and Holling 1990). Applications usually involve dynamic natural resource systems that are subject to only partially predictable environmental variation, along with other sources of uncertainty that limit effective management. The heart of adaptive decision making is the recognition of alternative hypotheses about resource dynamics, and an assessment of these hypotheses with monitoring data. A distinguishing feature is the use of management interventions as experimental treatments, the fundamental goal of which is to improve management.

Implementation Issues

Key issues in deciding when to use adaptive management are whether there is substantial uncertainty about the impacts on management, whether it is realistic to expect that we can reduce uncertainty, and whether reducing uncertainty can actually improve management. There is a growing interest in the role of resilience, the potential for surprise, and ways to accommodate these concerns in adaptive decision making.

A key concern is the recognition and measurement of success. An adaptive management project is viewed as successful if progress is made toward achieving management goals through the use of a learning-based (adaptive) decision process. Evaluation of an adaptive management project should involve a comparative assessment that considers the costs of adaptive management above and beyond those that would be incurred in any case. Impediments to the success of adaptive management include, e.g., institutional resistance to acknowledging uncertainty, risk aversion by many managers, myopic management, lack of stakeholder engagement, and other factors.

Learning organizations are critical in implementing adaptive management. For adaptive decision making, many organizations must make a transition from a more traditional "top down" organization structure to one that is more inclusive, collaborative, risk tolerant, and flexible (Gunderson 1999*b*, Stankey et al. 2005). However, an adaptive management approach must comply with statutory and regulatory requirements, most notably the National Environmental Policy Act.

Uncertainty and Learning

Four main types of uncertainty are used to characterize the influence of uncertainty on natural resource management in different ways. (*i*) Environmental variation refers to fluctuations in the physical environment, as expressed in precipitation patterns, temperature regimes, etc., which directly and indirectly influence the ecological and physical processes that determine resource dynamics. (*ii*) Partial controllability refers to the difference between the results intended by a given management decision and the results that actually occur. Unintended outcomes are often a result of management decisions implemented by indirect means. (*iii*) Partial observability expresses our inability to observe completely the resource system that is being managed, a nearly universal condition with renewable natural resources. (*iv*) Structural uncertainty expresses a lack of understanding (or lack of agreement) about the processes that control resource dynamics.

Models play a key role in representing uncertainty, by including hypotheses about how a resource system works and how it responds to management. Agreements, disagreements, and uncertainties about resource behaviors can be incorporated in models and used to guide investigations through basic research and learning-oriented management interventions. Uncertainty can be expressed by measures of model credibility, which evolve through time as monitoring data are assessed.

It is becoming increasingly clear that environmental conditions, and the ecological processes influenced by them, are exhibiting directional patterns of change. An obvious example is climate change, in which the environment is seen as evolving directionally in terms of temperature, precipitation and other variables, with associated changes in ecological structures and the processes controlling resource dynamics. It will be increasingly important to account for these patterns in developing management strategies.

Components of the Set-Up Phase of Adaptive Management

We draw upon our case studies to illustrate the elements and processes of adaptive management in the areas of climate change, water, energy, and human impacts on the landscape. The elements in the set-up phase of adaptive management include: stakeholder involvement, objectives, management alternatives, predictive models, and monitoring protocols.

Stakeholder involvement. Stakeholders bring different perspectives, preferences, and values to decision making. It is important to have at least some stakeholder engagement in all the set-up elements of a project, and to continue that engagement throughout the project. A critical challenge is to find common ground that will promote decision making despite disagreements among stakeholders about what actions to take and why. Failure to engage important stakeholders, and disagreement about how to frame a resource problem and identify its objectives and management alternatives, are common stumbling blocks.

Objectives. Successful implementation of adaptive management depends on a clear statement of project objectives. Objectives represent benchmarks against which to compare the potential effects of different management actions, and serve as measures to evaluate the effectiveness of management strategies.

Management alternatives. Adaptive decision making requires the clear identification of a set of potential alternatives from which to select an action at each decision point. Some actions might affect the resource directly; others might have indirect effects. Learning and decision making both depend on our ability to recognize differences in the consequences of different actions, which in turn offers the possibility of comparing and contrasting them in order to choose the best action.

Predictive models. Models play a critical role in adaptive management, as expressions of our understanding of the resource, as engines of ecological inference, and as indicators of the benefits, costs, and consequences of alternative management strategies. Importantly, they can represent uncertainty (or disagreement) about the resource system. Models are used to characterize resource changes over time, as the resource responds to fluctuating environmental conditions and management actions.

Monitoring protocols. Monitoring provides the information needed for both learning and evaluation of management effectiveness. The value of monitoring in adaptive management is inherited from its contribution to decision making. To make monitoring useful, choices of what ecological attributes to monitor and how to monitor them (frequency, extent, intensity, etc.), must be linked closely to the management situation that motivates the monitoring in the first place, as well as practical limits on staff and funding.

Components of the Iterative Phase of Adaptive Management

In the iterative phase of adaptive management, the elements in the set-up phase are folded into a recursive process of decision making, follow-up monitoring, assessment, learning and feedback, and institutional learning. Our case studies are used to illustrate these components in the areas of climate change, water, energy, and human impacts on the landscape.

Decision making. The actual process of adaptive decision making entails decisions at each point in time that reflect the current level of understanding and anticipate the future consequences of decisions. Decision making at each decision point considers management objectives, resource status, and knowledge about consequences of potential actions. Decisions are then implemented by means of management actions on the ground.

Follow-up monitoring. Monitoring provides information to estimate resource status, underpin decision making, and facilitate evaluation and learning after decisions are made. Monitoring is an ongoing activity, conducted according to the protocols developed in the set-up phase.

Assessment. The data produced by monitoring are used along with other information to evaluate management effectiveness, understand resource status, and reduce uncertainty about management effects. Learning is promoted by comparing predictions generated by the models with data-based estimates of actual responses. Monitoring data can also be compared with desired outcomes, in order to evaluate the effectiveness of management and measure its success in attaining management objectives.

Learning and feedback. The understanding gained from monitoring and assessment helps in selecting future management actions. The iterative cycle of decision making, monitoring, and assessment, repeated over the course of a project, leads gradually to a better understanding of resource dynamics and an adjusted management strategy based on what is learned.

Institutional learning. Periodically it is useful to interrupt the technical cycle of decision making, monitoring, assessment, and feedback in order to reconsider project objectives, management alternatives, and other elements of the set-up phase. This reconsideration constitutes an institutional learning cycle that complements, but differs from, the cycle of technical learning. In combination, the two cycles are referred to as "double-loop" learning.

Integrating the Components of Adaptive Management

Four projects are used as case studies to show how all the components are integrated in the application of adaptive management in the field: (*i*) management of river flows at the R.L. Harris Dam on the Tallapoosa River in Alabama; (*ii*) management of horseshoe crabs that provide food resources for migrating red knots in Delaware Bay; (*iii*) management of old-growth pine forests for breeding habitat of the endangered red-cockaded woodpecker; and (*iv*) management of human disturbance near nesting golden eagles in Denali National Park. Each example is comprehensive, in that it includes all the interacting components of adaptive management.

Future Directions

As the scope and complexity of resource problems grow, it will be increasingly important to make resource decisions in a structured and transparent way that is based on science and accounts for uncertainty. Because adaptive management meets these conditions, it can be a valuable template for effective decision making by managers in the DOI bureaus. Approaches currently in use in many government agencies "pre-adapt" them to adopting such a framework. For example, all DOI bureaus are engaged in both strategic planning and the tracking of results in plan implementation. Thus, their business practices already involve many of the important elements of adaptive management. A remaining need is to incorporate learning as a fundamental element of strategic planning and implementation, whereby the learning resulting from monitoring and assessment is fed back into future planning. By proactively linking plan implementation to plan development through a learning process, the adaptive cycle of learning-based management is completed and becomes standard business practice.

In recent years there has been steady growth in the engagement of stakeholders in bureau decision making. Active stakeholder engagement helps parties learn from each other, find areas of common ground, and build trust in developing management strategies collaboratively. Such an arrangement offers an incentive to stakeholders to agree on an initial strategy that involves compromise on all sides. In a context of adaptive decision making, negotiations to establish strategies allow parties to be more flexible because they recognize that the outcome of negotiations can be changed as understanding improves and conditions change. In this sense, a key challenge of adaptive management, namely the expression and treatment of uncertainty, can also be one of its strengths.

Two broad focus groups have worked more or less in parallel but independently to develop adaptive management of natural resources. One group focuses on technical issues (models, metrics and propagation of uncertainty, projection of the future consequences of present actions, optimal decision making in the face of uncertainty). The other group focuses on collaboration (institutions, stakeholders, cooperative interactions, elicitation of stakeholder values and perspectives). For the most part, researchers, practitioners, and even organizations tend to emphasize either one thrust or the other. The challenge is ultimately to join the two in a more unified vision and process, in which each reinforces and strengthens the other.

Opportunities for collaboration between adaptive management and emerging important fields of investigation are obvious. The developing field of ecosystem services can contribute to a framework for evaluating management impacts on the quantity and value of services provided by ecosystem attributes and processes. Resilience, vulnerability, and risk all have important roles in adaptive decision making, and their linkages need further examination and development. In particular, adaptive decision making has to be flexible and resilient enough to respond to the inevitable surprises that arise in resource management, because only then can ecosystems and their values be dependably maintained in the future.

Appendix of Case Study Overviews

The appendix contains paragraph-length thumbnail sketches of adaptive management projects used as examples in this guide. They range from translocation of endangered ducks in the Hawaiian islands, to restoration of Great Plains prairie potholes and New England shrub communities, to management of wetlands as waterbird habitat, to siting of renewable energy projects.

1. Introduction

In the early 21st century, the Department of the Interior (DOI) is presented with natural resource problems that are bigger, more complicated, and at the same time more uncertain than at any time in our history. The Department has enormous responsibilities that include managing one-fifth of the nation's land mass, 35,000 miles of coastline, and 1.76 billion acres of the Outer Continental Shelf. DOI upholds the federal government's trust responsibilities for 562 Indian tribes; conserves fish, wildlife, and their habitats; manages water supplies for more than 30 million people; and protects the icons of our national heritage.

DOI faces pressing challenges in meeting these responsibilities. Our dependence on foreign oil threatens our national security and our economy, and DOI can contribute to the development of domestically produced energy to help put an end to that dependence. But energy production must be done in a way that protects other resources such as fragile ecosystems and their components. We need more water than ever – for a growing population, farms, industry, businesses, and ecosystems – at a time when many watersheds have been degraded, droughts are increasing in frequency and severity, and freshwater supplies are dwindling. DOI must provide the leadership in finding new solutions to restore watersheds and equitably address competing demands for water so that people as well as the aquatic resources on which they depend can thrive. Every day there is another news story about the impacts of a changing climate on resources – extended droughts in river basins, the devastation of forests by wildfires, warming temperatures causing glaciers to melt, coasts and islands threatened by rising sea levels and fiercer storms. Identifying resources that are particularly vulnerable to climate change is a high-priority performance goal for DOI, along with implementing coordinated responses to these threats.

Given the scale of these challenges, and the uncertainty about the best courses of action in a complex environment, we need to change the way we address resource management. We must become more proactive in our approach to resource problems and how we manage resources sustainably. Collecting data and using our science capabilities to enhance understanding is crucial, but we cannot wait for perfect information to make decisions and take action. That would risk losing not just an opportunity, but in many cases the resources we are trying to protect.

A learning-based approach like adaptive management holds great promise for dealing with the challenges ahead. In fact, one of the goals in the DOI strategic plan (FY 2011–2016) calls for adaptive management as part of DOI's mission to provide a scientific foundation for decision making. Adaptive management involves the use of management in the spirit of experimental science to learn how to manage more effectively. It calls for explicit identification of objectives and alternative management strategies, and the involvement of stakeholders in making decisions. It feeds new information about management impacts back into the decision making process so that resource management can be adjusted on the basis of what is learned.

In this applications guide we describe how adaptive management can be applied in the areas that are critically important to DOI: water resources, energy, climate change, and human impacts on the landscape. We build on the framework for adaptive decision making described in the DOI Adaptive Management Technical Guide (Williams et al. 2007). The technical guide includes a discussion of the basic criteria for applying adaptive management as well as step-by-step descriptions of implementation. This applications guide is a companion document to the technical guide, yet it includes sufficient detail to be read as a stand-alone document.

The applications guide is intended to be useful to multiple audiences – from technical users who need information on particular issues such as components of uncertainty, to managers who want practical information on the sequence of steps involved in applying adaptive management. A key challenge is to describe adaptive management in terms general enough that its scope and breadth of application are apparent, while retaining the flavor of specific management projects and issues in the four thematic areas. The guide is not intended to be a detailed "cookbook" – in part because it would not be feasible to go into all the details of every project, and in part because every new application is unique and needs to be designed on an individual basis. Our hope is that readers will use the guide to envision the "who, what, when, where, and why" in applying adaptive management for their own particular resource issues.

After this introduction, we discuss the foundations of adaptive management and its components. Section 2 contains background and an overview of the elements of adaptive management, and Sections 3 and 4 discuss some issues that arise in its implementation. Sections 5 and 6 illustrate the components of adaptive management with examples from the thematic areas of water resources, energy, climate change, and human impacts on the landscape. Section 7 contains case studies showing the integration of individual components of adaptive management into a whole. Finally, we describe some future directions in the field of adaptive management. Readers may wish to skim portions of the guide and focus in more detail on the particular issues and examples of greatest interest to them.

In the guide we describe examples and case studies ranging from river flow management, to protecting migratory birds, to siting renewable energy projects. These examples, drawn from our four thematic focus areas, show the breadth of adaptive management applications at different scales and different levels of ecological complexity. On one hand, large-scale ecosystem management is shown by examples of rivers (e.g., Glen Canyon Dam; the Tallapoosa River), forests (e.g., fire fuel management in the Sierra Nevada; Biscuit Fire landscape management), and coral reefs (Great Barrier Reef marine zoning). In other examples, adaptive management is applied on the scale of an individual national wildlife refuge (e.g., native prairie restoration; prairie pothole restoration). Some applications apply broadly to multiple species and habitats (e.g., management of North American waterfowl) whereas others target a single species in a localized area (e.g., Laysan duck translocation; golden eagles in Denali National Park). The examples involve a variety of natural resources, including aquatic (e.g., Blanca wetlands; vernal pools), energy (e.g., solar facility siting and permitting; Cape Cod National Seashore wind turbines), and biological (e.g., endangered species such as Etowah River stream fishes or the Florida scrub-jay; Columbia River chinook salmon; forests of the Northwest). Taken together, the mixture of examples is intended to provide context and give the reader a feel for the operational principles common to applications of adaptive management. The appendix contains paragraph length thumbnail overviews of the projects used as examples.

2. Framework of Adaptive Management

The origin of adaptive management is rooted in parallel concepts from a variety of perspectives, including business (Senge 1990), experimental science (Popper 1968), systems theory (Ashworth 1982), and industrial ecology (Allenby and Richards 1994). In natural resources, the term simply means learning by doing, and adapting based on what's learned (Walters and Holling 1990). Adaptive management is based on the recognition that resource systems are only partially understood, and there is value in tracking resource conditions and using what is learned as the resources are being managed. Learning in adaptive management occurs through the practice of management itself, with adjustments as understanding improves.

2.1. Learning-Based Natural Resource Management

Natural resource managers and policy makers face the challenge of taking actions and making policy despite uncertainty about the consequences of management interventions. One well-known approach to resolving uncertainty is classical experimental science. Investigations using an experimental approach have been extraordinarily effective in analyzing natural resource systems, improving our understanding of ecological relationships, and increasing the accuracy of estimates of parameters in those relationships. An assumption in most applications of experimentation is that learning about the individual components of a system will eventually produce an understanding of how to manage it. In a classical approach to experimentation, science and management functions are usually separate – managers are presumed to know which components of the system need to be investigated, and scientists are presumed to know how to investigate those components. Unfortunately, this separation can present difficulties in attempts to understand and deal with today's large and complex problems. It can also impede the use of experimental learning for management adjustments, which is a critical and even definitive step in adaptive management.

Another approach to resolving uncertainty about the consequences is management by trial and error. Simply put, the idea is to try some management option, and if it doesn't perform as expected or desired, then try something else. The difficulty is that with all but the simplest systems a preferred option may not be obvious. If a selected option does not work as expected, there is no systematic mechanism to use what is learned from that experience as a guide for choosing follow-up options. Finally, there is no clear way to extrapolate site-specific learning to other sites. There are many cases in which trial and error has led to better management. However, the approach tends to be an inefficient way to advance learning and improve management, in large part because the rate of learning is unnecessarily slow. As a result, trial and error management can be costly (especially in terms of opportunity costs) and only marginally effective over unacceptably long periods of time.

In this guide, we describe the learning-based approach of adaptive management and illustrate its features by means of examples of some important problems facing resource managers and conservationists. We emphasize the importance of framing adaptive management problems as a structured process of iterative decision making (see, e.g., Gregory and Keeney 2002 for a discussion of structured decision making). We focus on examples that show how adaptive management can facilitate natural resource decision making and reduce the uncertainties that limit effective management. Because it acknowledges uncertainty and includes procedures to reduce uncertainty through the process of management itself, adaptive management can be applied to many pressing issues that need immediate attention, at local as well as larger scales. For many resource management problems, the use of management in an experimental, learning-oriented context may be the only feasible way to gain the understanding needed to manage more effectively.

The concept of adaptive decision making has been a part of natural resource management for several decades. One of the earliest discussions in the natural resource literature was by Beverton and Holt (1957), who described fisheries management in the following way:

> It is the changes produced in the fisheries by the regulations themselves ... that provide the opportunity of obtaining, by research, just the information that we may have been lacking previously. Thus the approach towards optimum fishing, and the increase in knowledge of where the optimum lies, can be two simultaneous and complementary advances; the benefits to the fisheries of such progress can hardly be exaggerated.

A generation later Holling (1978) and Walters and Hilborn (1978) provided the name and conceptual framework for adaptive management of natural resources, and Walters (1986) gave a more complete technical treatment of adaptive decision making. Lee's (1993) book expanded the context for adaptive management with comprehensive coverage of its social and political dimensions. These pioneering efforts sparked an interest in adaptive management that has grown steadily up to the present time. Many people in the field of natural resource conservation now claim, sometimes wrongly, that adaptive management is the approach they use to manage resources (Failing et al. 2004). The current popularity of adaptive management is somewhat at odds with its rather modest record of documented success, a record based at least in part on an inadequate framing of many management problems, poorly designed monitoring, and incomplete implementation of the adaptive process itself.

This applications guide builds on the framework of DOI Adaptive Management Technical Guide (Williams et al. 2007), which describes adaptive management in terms of the linkage of management with learning about natural resources. Here, we use examples to show how adaptive management can be used for both management and learning. We focus on practical applications in the areas of climate change, water, energy, and human impacts on the landscape.

2.2. Natural Resource Context for Adaptive Management

Adaptive management can be useful in cases where natural resources are responsive to management, but uncertainty exists about the impacts of management interventions. Applications usually involve the following general features (Figure 2.1).

- The natural resource system being managed is dynamic, with changes over time that occur in response to environmental conditions and management actions, which themselves vary over time. These factors can influence resource status directly as well as indirectly, through the ecological processes that drive resource changes.
- Environmental variation is only partly predictable, and is sometimes unrecognized. Variation in environmental conditions induces randomness in biological and ecological processes, which in turn leads to unpredictability in system behaviors.
- The resource system is subjected to periodic management interventions that may vary over time. Management actions influence resource system behaviors either directly or indirectly; for example, by altering system states such as resource size, or influencing ecological processes like mortality and movement, or altering vital rates like reproduction and recruitment rates.
- Effective management is limited by uncertainty about the nature of resource processes and the influence of management on them. Reducing this uncertainty can lead to improved management.

Many variations of these conditions are possible. For example, several different sites may be managed with actions taken at one location at a time, with information gained at one site used to inform subsequent decisions at other sites. Our example of solar project permitting illustrates this situation (see appendix). In another variation, different management actions may be taken simultaneously at different sites in the spirit of statistically designed experimentation, as illustrated by our example of landscape management strategies investigated by the Forest Service after the Biscuit Fire in Oregon (see appendix).

The role of time in this context is important. Management, environmental variation, resource status, and uncertainty are all expressed over time, which offers the prospect of management improvement by learning over the course of the management time frame.

Uncertainty and its effects. Uncertainty is always present in natural resource management, and it almost always limits management effectiveness to some degree. Representing and accounting for it in management is generally useful and sometimes critical (Bormann and Kiester 2004, Moore and Conroy 2006).

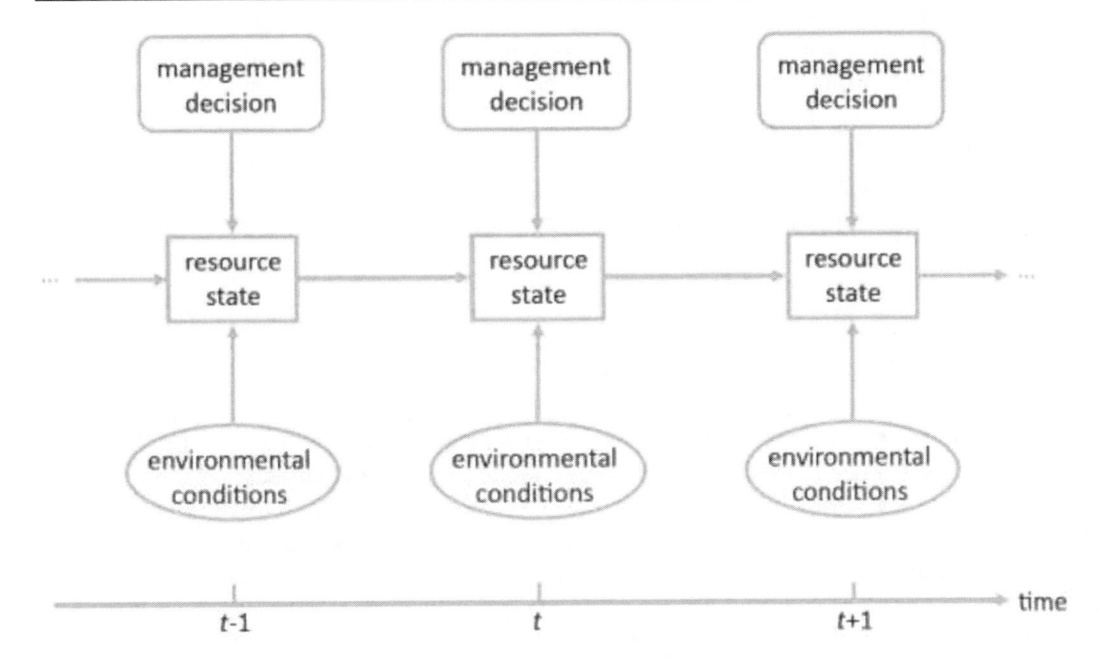

Figure 2.1. Dynamic resource system, with changes influenced by fluctuating environmental conditions and management actions. Management typically produces short-term returns (costs and (or) benefits) and longer-term changes in resource status.

Many sources and types of uncertainty are documented in the literature (e.g., Regan et al. 2002, Burgman 2005, Norton 2005, Le Treut et al. 2007). At a minimum, four kinds of uncertainty can influence the management of natural resource systems.

- *Environmental variation* is a prevalent source of uncertainty, which is largely uncontrollable and possibly not even perceived as such. It often has a dominating effect on natural resource systems, through factors such as climatic variability.
- *Partial observability* refers to our uncertainty about the actual status of a resource. The sampling variation that occurs during resource monitoring is an obvious example of partial observability.
- *Partial controllability* refers to the difference between the outcomes intended by decision makers and the outcomes that actually occur. This uncertainty can arise when indirect means (for example, regulations) are used to achieve an intended outcome (for example, a particular harvest or stocking rate). Partial controllability can lead to misrepresentation of management interventions, and thus to an inadequate accounting of their influence on resource behavior.
- *Structural or process uncertainty* refers to a lack of understanding – or lack of agreement among stakeholders – about the structure of the biophysical processes that control resource dynamics and the influence of management on them.

Environmental variation, partial observability, partial controllability, and structural uncertainty all limit our ability to manage natural resources effectively. In this guide we emphasize structural uncertainty, and the use of adaptive decision making to reduce it. It is reasonable to expect that learning will slow as the number and magnitudes of the uncertainties increase. Beyond some limit, uncertainty can become too great, learning too slow, and opportunity and other costs too high to justify a structured adaptive approach to decision making. This argues for an initial review of the uncertainties involved in the management of a resource system, and a realistic appraisal of the possibilities for learning, before adaptive management is put in place. We will return to the components of uncertainty in greater detail in Section 4.

2.3. Adaptive Decision Making Defined

A number of formal definitions have been advanced for adaptive management. For example, the National Research Council (2004) defines it as a decision process with

> … flexible decision making that can be adjusted in the face of uncertainties as outcomes from management actions and other events become better understood. Careful monitoring of these outcomes both advances scientific understanding and helps adjust policies or operations as part of an iterative learning process.

Published discussions of adaptive management variously emphasize experimentation (Lee 1993), uncertainty (Williams and Johnson 1995), science (Bormann et al. 2007), complexity (Allen and Gould 1986, Ludwig et al. 1993), management adjustments (Lessard 1998, Johnson 1999, Rauscher 1999), monitoring (Allen et al. 2001, Bormann et al. 2007), and stakeholder involvement (Norton 1995). In all cases adaptive management is seen as an evolving process involving learning (the accumulation of understanding over time) and adaptation (the adjustment of management over time). The sequential cycle of learning and adaptation leads naturally to two beneficial consequences: (*i*) better understanding of the resource system, and (*ii*) better management based on that understanding.

The feedback between learning and decision making is a defining feature of adaptive management. Thus, learning contributes to management by helping to inform decision making, and management contributes to learning by using interventions to investigate resources. Management interventions in adaptive management can be viewed as experimental "treatments" that are implemented according to a management design. However, the resulting learning should be seen as a means to an end – namely, effective management – and not an end in itself (Walters 1986). The ultimate focus of adaptive decision making is on management, and learning is valued for its contribution to improved management.

A distinction is often made between "passive" and "active" adaptive management (Salafsky et al. 1991, Bormann et al. 1996, Schreiber et al. 2004). Though there is considerable variability in the use of these terms (e.g., Williams 2011*b*), they are usually distinguished by the way uncertainty and learning are treated. As suggested by the wording, active adaptive management pursues the reduction of uncertainty actively through management interventions that emphasize rapid learning. On the other hand, passive adaptive management focuses less on the reduction of uncertainty and more on the status of the resource, with learning a useful by-product (Walters 1986). In practice the main difference between passive and active adaptive management is the degree to which management objectives emphasize the reduction of uncertainty (Williams 2011*b*).

Ambiguities in the use of these terms arise from the fact that there are several approaches to both active and passive adaptive management. For example, a common (but not the only) form of active adaptive management involves experimental management, in which decision making is focused on rapid learning (Williams 2011*b*). In this case different interventions are applied simultaneously at different sites in the spirit of designed experiments, with experimental learning used to guide future decision making. On the other hand, a common (but not the only) form of passive adaptive management involves decision making based on a single parameterized model. Here the focus is on achieving resource objectives, with little emphasis on learning per se. Different parameter values essentially represent different hypotheses about the effects of management, and learning occurs as data from post-decision monitoring are used to update the parameter distributions over repeated cycles.

Whatever the treatment of uncertainty, the heart of adaptive decision making is a recognition of alternative hypotheses about resource dynamics, and assessment of these hypotheses with monitoring data. These same features are shared with scientific investigation. That is, both science and adaptive management involve (*i*) the identification of competing hypotheses to explain observed patterns or processes; (*ii*) the use of models embedding these hypotheses to predict responses to experimental treatments; (*iii*) the monitoring of actual resource responses; and (*iv*) a comparison of actual versus predicted responses to gain better understanding (Williams 1997*a*, Nichols and Williams 2006). This overlap is the main reason that adaptive management is often referred to as a science-based approach to managing natural resources. Of course, a key difference between scientific investigation and adaptive decision making is that the treatments in adaptive management are management interventions chosen to achieve management objectives as well as learning, as opposed to experiments chosen for the pursuit of learning through hypothesis testing. Our case study of protecting nesting golden eagles in Denali National Park provides a good illustration of the scientific aspects of adaptive management.

Finally, it is useful to distinguish between adaptive management and the trial-and-error approach of "try something, and if it doesn't work try something else," which involves an ad hoc revision of strategy when it is seen as failing. In contrast to trial and error, adaptive management involves the clear statement of objectives, the identification of management alternatives, predictions of management consequences, recognition of uncertainties, monitoring of resource responses, and learning (National Research Council 2004). Basically, learning by ad hoc trial and error is replaced by learning through careful design and testing (Walters 1997). Adaptive management can be seen as a process of structured decision making (Williams et al. 2007), with special emphasis on iterative decisions that take uncertainty and the potential for learning into account. In later sections of this guide we develop the framework and components of adaptive management, with adaptive decision making seen as an iterative process of structured, objective-driven, learning oriented decision making that evolves as understanding improves.

We describe adaptive management as the interplay of decision and assessment components, in an iterative process of learning by doing and adapting based on what's learned. Adaptive management involves key activities such as stakeholder engagement, resource monitoring, and modeling, none of which is sufficient by itself to make a decision process adaptive. The integration of these components is what defines an adaptive approach to natural resource management. In Section 3.4 we compare and contrast adaptive management with alternative management approaches.

2.4. Conditions Warranting the Use of Adaptive Management

Not all resource management decisions can or should be adaptive. In some cases there is no chance to apply learning. In other cases, there is little uncertainty about what action to choose, or there are irreconcilable disagreements about objectives. But the concept of learning by doing is so intuitively appealing that the phrase "adaptive management" has been applied almost indiscriminately, with the result that many projects fail to achieve expected improvements. In many instances that failure may have less to do with the approach itself than with the inappropriate contexts in which it is applied (Gregory et al. 2006).

Whether or not a management problem calls for adaptive management is an important question that should be addressed at the outset of a project. In one form or another, the following five conditions are usually associated with adaptive management.

The first and most fundamental condition is that management is required in spite of uncertainty. In other words, the problem is important and timely enough that management action must be taken, though its consequences cannot be predicted with certainty.

Second, clear and measurable objectives are required to guide decision making. The articulation of objectives plays a critical role in evaluating performance as well as making decisions. Without useful objectives, and metrics by which they can be evaluated, it is difficult to determine what actions are best, and whether they are having the desired effect.

Third, there must be an opportunity to apply learning to management. Among other things this means that there is an acceptable range of management alternatives from which to make a selection, and a flexible management environment that allows for changes in management as understanding accumulates over time. It is the prospect of improved decision making that ultimately justifies adaptive management. Conversely, an adaptive approach is not warranted if potential improvements in management are insufficient to justify the costs of obtaining the information needed.

A fourth condition is that monitoring can be used to reduce uncertainty. The analysis and assessment of monitoring data result in better understanding of system processes and the opportunity to improve management based on that understanding. Without periodic monitoring of the relevant resource attributes, learning about resource responses and subsequent adjustment of management actions are not possible.

Finally, most expositions on adaptive management recognize the importance of a sustained commitment by stakeholders, including – but certainly not limited to – decision makers. Stakeholders should be actively involved throughout an adaptive management project, from the identification of objectives and management alternatives to the recognition of uncertainty and collection and analysis of monitoring data. Stakeholders are often diverse groups with different social, cultural, or economic perspectives. Active involvement means an ongoing commitment of time and resources by stake-holders (Lee 1999), among other things. Stakeholder engagement in discussions from the beginning of a project can help to reconcile polarized perspectives and facilitate collaboration in decision making. Our case study of flow management on the Tallapoosa River shows how stakeholders can become, and remain, deeply involved in all aspects of an adaptive management project.

2.5. Set-up Phase of Adaptive Management

Adaptive management can be described in terms of a set-up or planning phase during which some essential elements are put in place, and an iterative phase in which the elements are linked together in a sequential decision process (Figure 2.2). The iterative phase uses the elements of the set-up phase in an ongoing cycle of learning about system structure and function, and managing based on what is learned.

In this section we summarize the elements in the setup phase, namely stakeholder involvement, management objectives and options, predictive models, and monitoring protocols. Each of these elements has been described in greater detail in a companion publication, the DOI Adaptive Management Technical Guide (Williams et al. 2007).

Stakeholder involvement. A crucial step in any adaptive management application is to involve the appropriate stakeholders (Wondolleck and Yaffe 2000). It is particularly important for stakeholders to take part in assessing the resource problem and reaching agreement about its scope, objectives, and potential actions, even if differences of opinion about system responses remain.

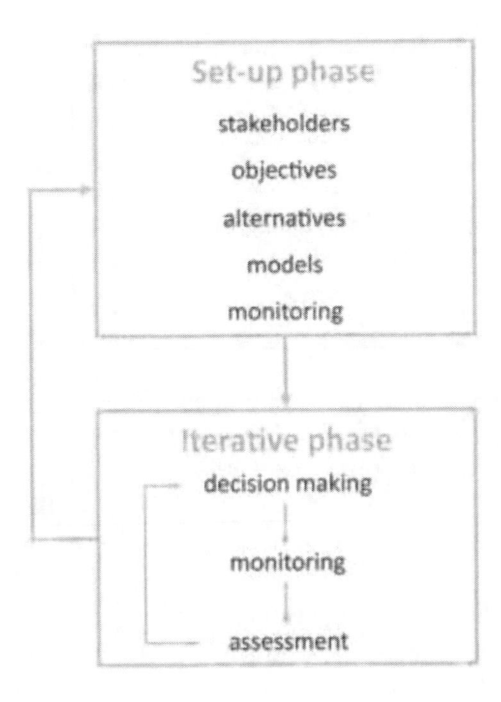

Figure 2.2. Two-phase learning in adaptive management. Technical learning involves an iterative sequence of decision making, monitoring, and assessment. Process and institutional learning involves periodic reconsideration of the adaptive management set-up elements.

Involving stakeholders in discussions at an early stage enhances their engagement in the management approach and highlights different stakeholder values, priorities, and perspectives. By defining the operating environment of an adaptive management project, stakeholders directly influence both decision making and learning. Adaptive decision making is not prescriptive about how many stakeholders there are, who they are, or what their perspectives or values are. The breadth and extent of stakeholder involvement can vary greatly among projects, and both are influenced by the scale and complexity of the problem (Comprehensive Everglades Restoration Plan Adaptive Management Integration Guide 2011).

In general, recognizing stakeholders' interests and ensuring their involvement are necessary for successful learning–based management. Frequently, decision making is undertaken without agreement, even among managers, about scope, objectives, and management alternatives. Without this agreement, management strategy is likely to be viewed as a reflection of partisan objectives or unnecessary constraints on decision making. The prospects for failure increase dramatically in such a situation.

Stakeholder involvement in an adaptive management project requires commitments as well as opportunities for involvement. Thus, stakeholders must commit to an agreed-upon process of reducing uncertainties and disagreements about the effects of management. That is, having reached agreement on the scope of the management problem and its objectives and potential interventions, stakeholders must then commit to an iterative process of objective-driven decision making. The failure of participants to make these commitments can impede and even undermine an adaptive management project.

Often there is value in engaging individuals who can facilitate these efforts or provide expertise from outside the stakeholder community of interest. Facilitators can bring novel insights into stakeholder interactions, just as outside experts can bring insights about resource systems. They thus can promote the development of better technical frameworks and more effective governance.

Objectives. Objectives play a critical role in evaluating performance, reducing uncertainty, and improving management over time. Clear and agreed-upon objectives are needed from the outset, to guide decision making and measure progress. To be useful, objectives should be specific, measureable within a recognizable time frame, and results-oriented (Williams et al. 2007).

Often there are multiple objectives. For example, a manager might simultaneously want to maintain species richness, maximize visitor use, allow harvest of one or more wildlife species, and minimize costs of all these activities. It then becomes important to weigh different objectives in terms of their perceived importance, in order to compare and prioritize management alternatives (Burgman 2005).

Management alternatives. Like any iterative decision process, adaptive decision making involves selecting a management action at each decision point, on the basis of the status of the resource at the time. Resource managers and other stakeholders, usually working with scientists, must identify the set of potential actions from which a selection is made.

The alternative management actions are an important element of an adaptive management project's operating environment because strategy choices are always limited by the set of available management options. If these options do not span a reasonable range of management actions, or if they fail to produce recognizably different patterns of system responses, adaptive management will be less useful in producing effective and informative strategies. This argues for careful thinking about the potential management actions to be included in a project.

Models. Models that link potential management actions to resource results play an important role in virtually all applications of structured decision making, whether adaptive or otherwise. Smart decision making requires one to compare and contrast management alternatives in terms of their costs and resource consequences. Models express benefits and costs in terms of management inputs, outputs, and outcomes. Of critical importance to adaptive management, they allow us to forecast the impacts of management.

Models also play a major role in representing uncertainty. In adaptive management, structural or process uncertainty is expressed by means of contrasting hypotheses about system structure and functions. These hypotheses are represented by different models that forecast resource changes. At any point, the available evidence will suggest differences in the adequacy of each model in characterizing resource dynamics. As evidence accumulates, our confidence in each model (and its associated hypothesis) evolves, through a comparison of model predictions with actual data from monitoring.

Monitoring protocols. The learning that is central to adaptive management occurs by comparing model-based predictions with observed responses. These comparisons allow us to learn about resource dynamics and discriminate among alternative hypotheses about resource processes and responses to management. By tracking useful measures of system response, well-designed monitoring programs facilitate evaluation and learning.

In general, monitoring in adaptive management provides data for four main purposes: (*i*) to evaluate progress toward achieving objectives; (*ii*) to determine resource status, in order to identify appropriate management actions; (*iii*) to increase understanding of resource dynamics by comparing predictions with actual monitoring data; and (*iv*) to develop and refine models of resource dynamics. Monitoring is much more efficient and effective to the extent that it is designed to meet these purposes.

The focus and design of monitoring in adaptive management should be inherited from the larger management context of which monitoring is a part. The value of monitoring stems from its contribution to adaptive decision making, and monitoring efforts should be designed with that goal in mind (Nichols and Williams 2006).

Because the set-up elements just described are folded directly into the process of decision making, they need to be stated and agreed upon at the beginning of an adaptive management application. Of course, the elements themselves can change over time, as ecological conditions and stakeholder perspectives – and possibly the composition of the stakeholder group – evolve (see Section 2.7). For this reason the set-up phase is also referred to as "deliberative," to indicate the potential for changes in one or more elements.

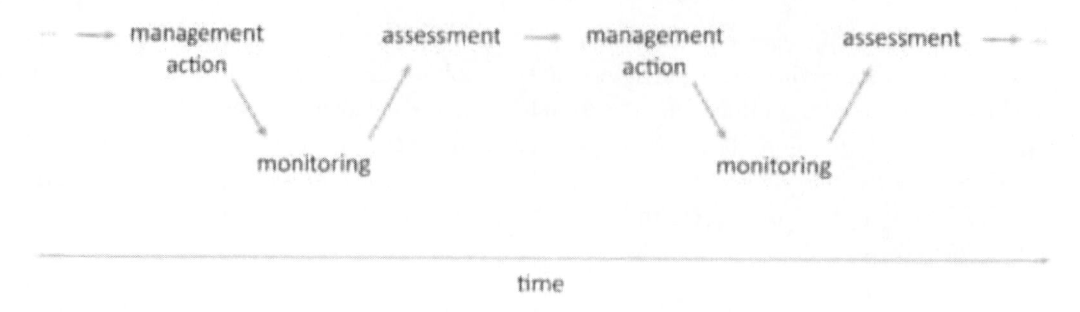

Figure 2.3. Iterative phase of adaptive management. Management actions are based on objectives, resource status, and understanding. Data from follow-up monitoring are used to assess impacts and update understanding. Results from assessment guide decision making at the next decision point.

2.6. Iterative Phase of Adaptive Management

The operational sequence of adaptive management incorporates the set-up elements in an iterative decision process. Figure 2.3 shows the components of management. Steps in the iteration are described as follows.

Decision making. At each decision point in time, an action is chosen from the set of available management alternatives. Management objectives are used to guide this selection, given the state of the system and the level of understanding when the selection is made. Actions are likely to change through time, as understanding increases and the resource system responds to environmental conditions and management. That is, management is adjusted in response to both changing resource status and learning. The influence of reduced uncertainty (or greater understanding) on decision making is what makes the decision process adaptive.

Follow-up monitoring. Monitoring is used to track resource changes, and in particular to track responses to management over time. In the context of adaptive management, monitoring is an ongoing activity, producing data to evaluate management interventions, update measures of model confidence, and prioritize management options.

Assessment. The information produced by monitoring folds into performance evaluation, learning, and future decision making. For example, the comparison of model predictions with data from monitoring is a critical part of learning. The degree to which the predictions match observed changes serves as an indicator of model adequacy. Confidence increases in models that predict change accurately, and confidence decreases in models that do not. In this way evidence accumulates for the hypotheses that best represent resource dynamics.

As important as it is, learning is not the only valuable outcome of analysis and assessment in adaptive management. Comparison of predicted and actual outcomes can also be used to evaluate the effectiveness of management and measure its success in attaining objectives. In addition, comparisons of projected costs, benefits, and impacts help to identify useful management alternatives.

Learning and feedback. At each particular time, the understanding gained from monitoring and assessment guides the choice of management actions. As understanding evolves, so does decision making based on that understanding. In this way, the iterative cycle of decision making, monitoring, and assessment leads gradually to better management as a consequence of better understanding.

2.7. Institutional Learning

Adaptive decision making not only gives us the chance to learn about ecological structures and functions, but also about the decision process itself. Learning about the "architecture" of decision making is accomplished by periodically recycling through the elements in the set-up phase (Figure 2.2) and adjusting the elements as needed to account for evolving stakeholder perspectives and institutional arrangements. The broader context of learning that also recognizes uncertainty about these elements in the decision process is sometimes called institutional or "double-loop" learning (Argyris and Shon 1978, Salafsky et al. 2001).

The need to revisit and adjust the set-up elements of adaptive management often becomes more pressing as adaptive management proceeds over time. Stakeholder perspectives and values can shift as adaptive management progresses, previously unanticipated patterns in resource dynamics are exposed, and changes occur in social and cultural values and norms. Any of these changes can lead to adjustment of objectives, alternatives, and other set-up elements. In this sense, learning in adaptive management can focus on changes in institutional arrangements and stakeholder values as well as changes in the resource system itself.

A well-designed project provides a chance to learn at both levels. The technical learning in Figure 2.2 ideally occurs over a relatively short term during which objectives, alternatives, and other set-up elements remain unchanged. On the other hand, learning about the decision process itself occurs through periodic revisiting of the set-up elements over the longer term. If changes in the set-up elements are made as often as changes in management actions, these effects may become confounded and impede learning at either level.

3. Implementation Issues

The DOI Adaptive Management Technical Guide (Williams et al. 2007) touched on a number of important issues that are relevant to adaptive management applications and merit a more detailed discussion here. One issue involves scale, especially spatial and ecological scale, and the applicability of adaptive management across scales. The role of resilience, the potential for surprise, and ways to accommodate these concerns are also germane to adaptive decision making. Other issues include an accounting of costs and benefits in adaptive decision making, and the nature and role of learning organizations in implementing adaptive management.

3.1. Geographic Scale

One concern in applications of adaptive management is the appropriate scale for decision making. Adaptive management is most visibly associated with big-picture applications that have a high degree of complexity. Prominent examples that refer to adaptive management include:

- river management (Columbia, Platte, and Missouri Rivers [Quigley and Arbelbide 1997, Wissmar and Bisson 2003, Levine 2004, Williams 2006, Freeman 2010]; Glen Canyon Dam on the Colorado River [Melis et al. 2006, U.S. Geological Survey 2008]);
- regional forest management (Rapp 2008, Reeves et al. 2006);
- continental waterfowl harvest management (Williams and Johnson 1995, Williams 2006);
- commercial fisheries (Hilborn 1992, Conover and Munch 2002);
- broad-scale habitat management (National Ecological Assessment Team 2006);
- pest management in forest ecosystems (Shea et al. 2002); and
- water management (Everglades [Holling et al. 1994, Comprehensive Everglades Restoration Plan Adaptive Management Implementation Guide 2011]).

Ecosystem management at this scale involves economic, social, institutional, and ecological linkages across large landscapes with a high degree of heterogeneity. One implication is that these systems are likely to respond in unexpected ways to variable environmental conditions and management practices. Because large ecosystems are susceptible to surprise, adaptive management seems especially appropriate. The importance and high visibility of such projects have led many people to believe that adaptive management only applies to large-scale, complex problems.

However, adaptive decision making as we describe it here applies equally well to local issues, as long as the basic conditions are met (e.g., see Williams et al. [2007], Moore et al. [2011], and Knutson et al. [2011] for examples). Our case study of red knots and horseshoe crabs in the Delaware Bay illustrates this point. There are probably many more potential applications of adaptive management at local scales, not only because of the prevalence of such problems but also because they can often be framed more easily, their uncertainties can be identified more readily, stakeholder involvement can be facilitated more directly, and management can often be implemented more easily (McConnaha and Paquet 1996).

The point here is that the activities involved in structuring a decision problem and trying to improve management through learning are not in themselves limited by the scale of the problem. Clearly, the specific approaches and procedures used to identify and incorporate the elements in an adaptive application can vary considerably across scales. For example, a local problem with only a few stakeholders, a single objective, and a single source of uncertainty about the impacts of management may require approaches that differ considerably from those needed for a large-scale problem with many stakeholders, multiple objectives, and several sources of uncertainty. Nonetheless, both problems are amenable to a structured, adaptive approach to decision making. Rather than scale, the main issues in deciding when to use adaptive management are whether there is substantial uncertainty about the impacts on management, whether it is realistic to expect that we can reduce uncertainty, and whether reducing uncertainty can actually improve management.

3.2. Surprise, Resilience and Flexibility

Surprise, expressed as a "disconnect" between the ecosystem behaviors we expect and those that actually occur (Gunderson 1999*b*), is a feature of virtually all ecosystems. It can arise in several ways. For example, an ecosystem may be poorly understood, or changing environmental conditions may induce new behaviors, or the ecosystem may evolve new responses to management interventions. Within limits, surprise can be anticipated, managed, and reduced. However, it can never be eliminated, even when management is learning-based and carefully framed in terms of objectives, alternatives, and predicted consequences of actions. For example, Peterson et al. (2003) used an example of lake eutrophication to illustrate how an inadequate representation of structural uncertainty, in which critical ecosystem features were not represented in the models, resulted in management that would inadvertently lead to aperiodic cycles of stability and ecological collapse as thresholds to different states of the aquatic system were crossed. The unexpected impact of an invasive species is another example of surprise. In natural resource management the potential for surprise is always there because we never know everything about a resource system, and it never stops adapting to changing circumstances.

One approach that is sometimes proposed to address ecological surprise involves broad-scale surveillance monitoring. The argument is that such monitoring can serve as an "early warning" system for the surprises that inevitably arise as resources respond to changes in large-scale environmental drivers like climate and land use. The challenge is how to design such a monitoring program, i.e., how to develop effective and efficient monitoring to highlight unknown and unanticipated resource patterns. Because surprises are by definition not predictable, answers to the basic design questions about what, where, when, and how to monitor are not available to guide the monitoring design. That said, any monitoring effort, no matter how it is focused and targeted, presents the opportunity for discovery of unanticipated knowledge. It therefore is smart to explore the data produced by any monitoring effort, including the data produced in adaptive management, for novel patterns and relationships.

Surprise, and the associated issues of uncertainty and resilience, are of major importance in a growing literature that comes under the rubric of "resilience thinking" (Gunderson et el. 1995, Gunderson and Holling 2002, Walker and Salt 2006). The framework of resilience thinking includes the following elements.

- Natural systems are subject not only to reversible short-term change, but also to long-term change that is effectively irreversible. Ecological thresholds exist beyond which reversible change becomes irreversible.
- Ecosystem evolution is characterized by changes across scales that are surprising and often unpredictable.
- Patterns of transformation in ecosystems are driven by slow accumulation of natural and cultural capital followed by rapid reorganization, which leads to disruption of the ecosystem and an increased potential for it to be restructured.
- Ecosystem management can use the principles and practices of adaptive management for learning and adaptive change.

An important conclusion of resilience thinking is that management focusing on only one or a few ecosystem attributes can lead to loss of resilience and an increased vulnerability to unexpected and destructive change. Well-known examples include the intensive management of grazing, which can increase the vulnerability of grasslands to drought; the broad-scale control of certain pests, which can increase the likelihood of devastating outbreaks of other pests; water management for irrigation and flood control, which can increase the vulnerability of riverine systems to large-scale flooding; and intensive management of commercial fishing, which can lead to the unexpected collapse of a commercial fishery. Surprises like these usually are a result of managing in ways that induce stability in targeted ecosystem components in the short term but lead to the loss of ecosystem resilience over the long term, and increase the vulnerability of the system to extremes such as drought, floods, and other major random events.

Some steps can be taken to deal with surprise in the management of ecosystems.

- Expect and account for surprise in decision making. In particular, recognize that in any managed ecosystem, uncertainty and the potential for surprise are implicit in the scenarios under consideration.
- Incorporate models that are based on broadly differing assumptions, with broadly differing predictions.
- Retain enough management flexibility to adapt to surprise when it occurs.
- Manage the system for sufficient resilience to maintain structure and function when external shocks occur.
- Increase the range of ecosystem conditions, management alternatives, and sources of evidence that are considered.
- Use experimental management and monitoring to learn and manage adaptively.

Among other things, a robust application of adaptive management should consider important cross-scale factors and effects when framing a project. There is always some risk in assuming that future system behaviors will mimic those of the past, and in fact, management itself can induce changes in system resilience. It is smart to take these issues into account when formulating an adaptive management project and designing monitoring and assessment.

3.3. Evaluating Adaptive Management

Although many people have pointed out the limited success of adaptive management in natural resource management (e.g., Stankey et al. 2003, Stankey and Clark 2006), there are no broadly accepted standards by which to recognize and measure success. Weinstein et al. (1997) proposed success criteria for specific types of projects such as large-scale wetland restoration efforts, and Marmorek et al. (2006) developed the concept of enabling or inhibiting factors as a way to classify factors that affect adaptive management project success. O'Donnell and Galat (2008) articulated and evaluated some success criteria for adaptive management of riverine systems.

In the DOI Adaptive Management Technical Guide (Williams et al. 2007) a straightforward standard for recognizing success in adaptive management projects was proposed. An adaptive management project is viewed as successful if progress is made toward achieving management goals through the use of a learning-based (adaptive) decision process. This standard contains two essential elements: progress toward achieving objectives, a primary indicator of success for any management strategy; and the use of learning-based management, with the integration of stakeholder involvement, targeted monitoring, agreed-upon objectives, management alternatives, and projections of consequences into an iterative learning cycle.

On the basis of this standard, four criteria were identified for successful implementation in the DOI Adaptive Management Technical Guide.

- First, recognizable progress must be made in achieving management objectives over a reasonable time frame. Of course, management objectives will not always be met with certainty; for example, the outcomes of local management can be masked by larger-scale processes outside the control of management decision making. Thus, management must be judged by the *process* of decision making as well as short-term progress toward desired results.
- Second, monitoring and assessment results must be used to adjust and improve management decisions. The linkage of monitoring and assessment to objective-driven decision making is what defines adaptive management and allows its long-term benefits to be realized. When learning is folded into future management, that in itself is an indicator of success.
- Third, stakeholders must be actively involved in and committed to the decision making process. This involvement provides a solid foundation for learning-based management and builds support for it. It also gives resource managers the chance to obtain additional information about the resource system and priorities for management.
- Finally, the implementation of adaptive management must be consistent with applicable laws and regulations. This is very important for projects that include federal and state partners and involve statutes like the National Environmental Policy Act, Endangered Species Act, and the Federal Advisory Committee Act (Rodgers 1979).

Costs and benefits. A common criticism of adaptive management is that it demands time and resources. Everyone who has attempted adaptive management knows that engaging stakeholders over the life of a project takes time and effort. Everyone knows that reaching consensus about objectives and management options can be difficult and frustrating, in large part because stakeholders often come to negotiations with strong opinions about what actions to take and what outcomes to expect (Wondolleck and Yaffe 2000). Everyone is aware of the difficulties involved in problem framing, modeling, and identification of uncertainty.

Though the costs of stakeholder engagement, problem framing, monitoring, and so on sometimes seem prohibitive, the costs associated with not making these investments are often unrecognized or unacknowledged (Wildavsky 1988). Without a learning-based approach, management improvements, if they occur at all, accumulate more slowly, thus leaving the system vulnerable to surprising and potentially disruptive behaviors. Among other things, a lack of agreement by stakeholders about scope, objectives, and interventions can by itself cause the project to fail and lead to litigation. In this case the project implementation can be delayed, costs can skyrocket, and the loss of long-term ecosystem values can be very high.

While adaptive management does involve a commitment of time and resources, these costs are compensated by future benefits from better understanding and increased flexibility in dealing with surprise. This contrasts with management in the absence of an active engagement of stakeholders or a consistent framing of the scope, objectives, and other elements of a structured approach. An appropriate analysis of the value of adaptive management involves a comparative assessment of its benefits and costs, including opportunity costs, relative to the benefits and costs of non-adaptive management.

As mentioned earlier, the benefits of adaptive management include management improvements that result from better understanding. But learning also produces external benefits because the knowledge gained from an adaptive management project can be applied to other problems in different settings. How great the external benefits are depends on how significant the knowledge is, and how broadly it is used in other management settings.

In terms of costs, an accurate accounting would include direct management costs as well as the costs of monitoring and working with stakeholders. A simple, non-comparative analysis produces a biased accounting of adaptive management costs because it doesn't recognize the fact that many of the project costs attributed to adaptive management would also be incurred with non-adaptive management. A comparative assessment would consider the costs of adaptive management above and beyond those that would be incurred in any case. This kind of assessment is complicated by the fact that monitoring and stakeholder involvement can change the benefits as well as the costs.

We propose the following comparative evaluation of benefits and costs, at the level of projects considered individually or in a broader ecosystem context.

At the project level, costs and benefits of an adaptive approach are compared directly to the costs and benefits of a non-adaptive approach to the project. Because monitoring and stakeholder involvement almost always occur at some level in non-adaptive projects, evaluations should focus on any extra costs incurred specifically by the adaptive approach. A careful analysis of costs associated with monitoring and stakeholder involvement may show that the costs of adaptive management are actually less than those of non-adaptive management, over the long term.

At a larger scale, the systematic evaluation of adaptive management addresses the benefits and costs of a group of projects considered as part of a larger ecosystem. As in project-level evaluations, the focus is on comparing adaptive management with other management approaches. However, here the external benefits become more significant, because what is learned from one project can be applied to related projects, and the diffusion of knowledge to other projects becomes an important issue. Adaptive management in a larger systematic context also can lead to reduced monitoring costs as knowledge gained from one project benefits another, thereby reducing the need for duplication of effort. At this level, opportunities for economies of scale from geospatial coordination can be significant. As the problems in managing ecosystems increase in scale and complexity, the advantages of applying adaptive management systematically are also likely to become greater and more apparent.

It is worth re-emphasizing that adaptive management is designed to yield insights about natural resources and their responses to management as interventions occur through time. The process produces improved understanding and management gradually, as monitoring data are assessed and uncertainty is reduced. Among other things, this means that the time frame for an adaptive management project should be long enough to allow for the learning process. Consideration of the necessary time commitment for adaptive management should be a key point of negotiation in deciding whether to use the approach.

3.4. Impediments and Alternatives to Adaptive Management

Regardless of the features that recommend adaptive management, its use in the real world of natural resource management is still evolving. Where it is applied, the view is sometimes that adaptive decision making does not add significant value. If adaptive management makes so much sense in concept, why has it not been implemented more frequently and successfully?

The literature on adaptive management points out many impediments to its success (e.g., McLain and Lee 1996, Walters 1997, Gregory et al. 2006). A partial list includes the following.

- A complex decision making structure must be in place or be put in place, and technical expertise and support must be available for people who implement adaptive management. Establishing this type of decision making framework can involve considerable up-front costs.
- There often is institutional resistance to acknowledging uncertainty. Many managers feel that acknowledging uncertainty is tantamount to an admission that they are not competent.
- Managers often believe they already know the actions that are needed, and follow-up monitoring and assessment are unnecessary activities using resources that could be put to better use for conservation on the ground.
- Many people believe that they are already using adaptive management, even when they are not. This occurs most often with projects that involve some ongoing monitoring, in the mistaken belief that monitoring by itself is enough to make a project "adaptive."
- There is extreme risk aversion by many managers, which leads to strategies that are risk-aversive in the near term, with little or no opportunity for learning.
- Management often is short-sighted, emphasizing near-term gains and losses and devaluing long-term management benefits and costs. If the future is heavily discounted, there is little incentive to use adaptive management to learn how to manage better in the future.
- Stakeholders are not engaged in a meaningful way. Without direct involvement, stakeholders can become disillusioned with management practices, withhold support for a project, or mount legal challenges. Yet many managers are reluctant to include stakeholders in decision making.
- There is a lack of institutional commitment to follow through with the necessary monitoring and assessment after an initial start-up of adaptive decision making. Monitoring activities include sampling design, data collection and summarization,

database management, and data assessment. Many managers are unable or unwilling to continue these activities for extended periods of time.

These and other impediments (overlapping jurisdictions; conflicting priorities among scientists, decision makers, and stakeholders) can be enough to prevent the successful implementation of adaptive management (McLain and Lee 1996, Walters 1997, Rogers 1998).

With all these challenges, an obvious question is what are the alternatives to adaptive management? Several have been identified (Williams 1997*b*).

- Ad hoc management. This approach could also be called seat-of-the-pants decision making, based on some combination of anecdotal information, the absence of clear management goals, little or no technical foundation for management actions, and inadequate monitoring. It is a variation of trial-and-error management.
- Wait-and-see management. Managers using this approach refrain from interventions for extended periods of time on the assumption that natural variation will provide enough information to understand the consequences of management. The approach avoids the potential for negative impacts of active management, but does not account for decision making and the possibility of learning and resource sustainability through management.
- Steady-state management. With this approach managers take their best guess at an optimal resource state and look for management actions to eliminate deviations from that state. Above and beyond the obvious problem that there really are no equilibrium conditions in natural resources, steady-state management confounds environmental conditions and management impacts, and thereby limits the opportunity to learn by means of management (see Williams 1997*b*, Gunderson 1999*a*). Eventually it leads to loss of resilience and increasing vulnerability to external shock (Gunderson and Holling 2002).
- Conventional state-specific management. This approach involves the use of explicit objectives and models. The approach is based on an assumption that the objectives are appropriate, the resource system is fully observed and understood, and the resource models reflect full understanding. New data are used to track the system's current status; however, structural uncertainty and surprise are not accounted for in the assessment of management alternatives. The problem is that uncertainty is almost always present, though often not explicitly expressed and sometimes not recognized.

Under the right circumstances, most of these management approaches can be appropriate. Non-adaptive management is reasonable if there is little uncertainty about what actions to take and what results to expect, if effective monitoring is not possible, or if there is no way to feed results of monitoring and assessment back into management strategy. An adaptive approach can be successful only when the basic requirements for implementation can be met (Williams et al. 2007). When they cannot be met, an alternative approach may be more useful and less costly. However, keep in mind that resource systems are never fully understood, and there is always the possibility of unexpected consequences of a management strategy. Even if non-adaptive management is used, it is smart to engage stakeholders actively and maintain enough flexibility in management practice to change the management strategy when the need becomes obvious.

3.5. Organizations and Adaptive Learning

Adaptive management flourishes in an environment in which surprise is anticipated, learning is promoted, and participatory decision making is the norm (Stankey et al. 2005). But in spite of frequent assertions that adaptive management is being used, and frequent descriptions of learning as an element of management, there has been only limited progress in promoting a connection between learning and management. Documentation of the institutional structures and processes needed to make an adaptive approach work is also limited (Mclain and Lee 1994). For adaptive decision making, organizations must make a transition from the more traditional "command and control" structure to one that is more inclusive, collaborative, risk tolerant, and flexible (Gunderson 1999*b*, Stankey et al. 2005). The difficulties of making that transformation, including the sustained commitment of leadership and the staffing of skilled practitioners at the field level, should not be underestimated.

An institution's recognition of uncertainty as an inherent part of natural resource management is very important. Some hold that adaptive management is not feasible unless the management institutions are willing to embrace uncertainty (Gunderson et al. 1995). Among other things, the embrace of uncertainty means accepting that different viewpoints exist and involving stakeholders with different perspectives in identifying and addressing uncertainties.

At issue here is the structure and context of a learning-oriented organization that can facilitate adaptive decision making. Attributes of a learning organization include the following (Senge 1990, Fulmer 2000, Michael 1995):

- acknowledgement that the world is uncertain and that it often is impossible to predict outcomes accurately;
- realization of the importance of training people in the group process skills needed to work effectively in cross-disciplinary teams;
- positive reinforcement and rewards for experimentation and learning; and
- recognition that surprises and even crises can be opportunities for learning.

Many observers think that the major challenges in adopting adaptive management are fundamentally institutional (Stankey et al. 2005). Institutions are built on major premises and long-held beliefs that are deeply embedded in educational systems, laws, policies, and norms of professional behavior (Miller 1999). There is a natural tension between the tendency of large, long-standing organizations to maintain a strong institutional framework for thinking and decision making, versus adaptive decision making that relies on collaboration and flexibility, awareness of alternative perspectives, acceptance of uncertainty, and use of participatory decision making (Gunderson 1999*a*).

Structuring an organization for learning-based management can be hampered by the widespread belief that adaptive management does not constitute a significant departure from past practices, and involves little more than occasionally changing management actions (Stankey and Clark 2006). One consequence is that not enough attention is paid to institutional barriers, and not enough effort is spent on designing organizational structures and processes to accommodate an adaptive style of management. At a minimum, it is necessary to rethink the notions of risk and risk aversion, and establish conditions that encourage and reward learning by individuals.

3.6. Statutory and Regulatory Considerations

Adaptive management is an open process of decision making in which stakeholders are directly engaged and decision making authority is shared among them. One requirement is that objectives and other elements of the decision process are stated explicitly and that they remain open to analysis and debate. A crucial feature is learning over time, and adjusting decisions as understanding improves. However, the use of an adaptive management approach does not preclude the necessity of complying with the statutory and regulatory requirements that apply to a particular program or project. For example, the adaptive management process for dam relicensing should account for the requirements of the Federal Energy Regulatory Commission, or the requirements for the Endangered Species Act and its implementing procedures.

A particular example is the effort by the Fish and Wildlife Service to integrate adaptive management principles into habitat conservation plans under Section 10 of the Endangered Species Act. In this guide, our example of fish conservation in the Etowah River (see appendix) illustrates how this can work. In another example, relicensing of dams by the Federal Energy Regulatory Commission may call for adaptive management to adjust flow regimes as information is gathered about flow impacts on aquatic species at risk. The study of the dam on the Tallapoosa River, described in Section 7, is a case in point. Under certain conditions, it is possible to make a permitting process adaptive at the programmatic level. Our examples of energy infrastructure siting and operations suggest how knowledge gained at one site can be applied systematically to decision making at other sites.

Any anticipated federal decision making contemplated in an adaptive management approach to natural resource management must be supported by analysis prepared according to the requirements of the National Environmental Policy Act (NEPA). Care must be taken to structure analysis pursuant to NEPA, which may include preparation of an environmental impact statement, to support the decision making contemplated in an adaptive approach to management.

In all these cases, agency officials should invest significant effort in assessing legal issues at two critical stages of adaptive management: (*i*) at the time a decision is made to use adaptive management for a particular project, and (*ii*) at the time the agency seeks to adjust management decisions based on the information derived from monitoring and assessment. Knowing what federal laws and regulations require, and what limitations apply before agency decisions are made, allows stakeholders to anticipate the legal requirements and integrate them into an adaptive management process. Of course, it is important to recognize that some laws and implementing regulations prescribe specific activities and assessments that could limit or even preclude the use of adaptive management.

National Environmental Policy Act. One of the most important statutes for an agency to consider as it implements adaptive management is NEPA. The primary goal of this statute is to ensure that agency decision makers and the public recognize and account for environmental and other related impacts of proposed agency actions. Compliance with NEPA generally involves a series of specific procedural steps, and certain NEPA processes involve public participation and public review and comment on the agency's proposed action and its environmental consequences as disclosed through the NEPA process. In general, federal agencies can take three approaches to compliance with NEPA, depending on the relative significance of environmental consequences anticipated to result from the agency's proposed action. An environmental impact statement (EIS) is required whenever an agency proposes a "major federal action significantly affecting the quality of the human environment." An EIS must include an analysis of alternatives to the proposed action. The actions contemplated for implementation in a particular adaptive management process may rise to the level of a major federal action requiring preparation of an EIS. Other less complex or controversial actions may be addressed under NEPA by a less comprehensive environmental assessment (EA). Under NEPA, the completion of an EA will result either in the identification of possibly significant impacts of the proposed action (and the need to prepare an EIS), or can support a "finding of no significant impact." Finally, some proposed actions can be categorically excluded from preparation of an EIS or EA, if provided for in an agency's NEPA implementing procedures.

An EIS incorporating adaptive management needs to describe clearly how the approach would be implemented. This not only includes the types of actions that are proposed initially, but also the results that are anticipated from monitoring and assessment, and future actions that may be implemented on the basis of those results. Decision makers and the public must be able to see how the adaptive management approach would be implemented, including potential future actions and anticipated impacts on the environment. The anticipated impacts of such potential future actions may either be analyzed in NEPA analysis prepared at the point of the initial decision to take an adaptive approach, or may be considered in NEPA analysis prepared to support a new decision or decisions when it becomes clear, as a result of monitoring and assessment, that such actions are warranted.

As acknowledged in guidance issued by the Department's Office of Environmental Policy and Compliance (ESM No. 10-20, April 23, 2010), adaptive management and NEPA share an emphasis on learning. A common challenge in making adaptive management work in natural resource decision making is that ongoing monitoring and assessment may reveal new information that requires a new decision to be made to alter the management situation. A proposal to make a new decision or take a new action triggers the requirement to comply with NEPA. If the EIS or other NEPA analysis is prepared at the outset of the project using an adaptive management approach, and it anticipates additional decision making and analyzes the possible environmental consequences of subsequent decision making at the outset, then it may be that no new analysis is needed for purposes of NEPA compliance (see 43 CFR 46.145).

In the event that the NEPA documentation prepared at the outset of the project does not, or can not (because of uncertainty), provide such analysis, then additional analysis must be prepared pursuant to NEPA in order to display and analyze the new learning upon which a new set of alternatives is available for decision making. In such a case, the agency may elect to prepare an EA or EIS, which may, if appropriate, be "tiered to," or incorporate by reference, material from the previously prepared NEPA analysis (see 40 CFR 1508.28, 43 CFR 46.140), in order to support the new decisions to be made. In some circumstances, depending on the way the decisional space has been framed, the agency may elect, or may even be required, to prepare a supplement to the NEPA analysis supporting the existing decision, in order to support the new or changed decision (see 40 CFR 1502.9[c]).

When describing alternatives in an EIS, two important issues should be taken into account. The first focuses on the range of impacts of the management alternatives. Here, the effects on the resource can be estimated by analyzing the alternatives that are most and least intrusive, along with a non-action option. These alternatives should encompass the range of impacts and successes associated with the remaining alternatives. By considering such a range of alternatives, one avoids the possibility of choosing an alternative that exceeds the limits of the original analysis, which would trigger additional NEPA review (citation http://ceq.hss.doe.gov/ ntf/report/chapter4.pdf).

The second issue focuses on the potential effects of an array of potential management alternatives and the conditions that would lead to the selection of one of them. That is, the effects of each potential alternative are individually analyzed, including specification of the data that lead to selection of the chosen alternative. If effectively planned, an EIS will cover a wide enough range of future possibilities and a clear prescription of the conditions for their use, to preclude the need for additional NEPA analysis, documentation, and public involvement in the future. The overall goal is to analyze the impacts of different management alternatives in a way that sustains maximum flexibility in selecting the appropriate option without triggering the requirement for a new or supplemental NEPA review.

4. Uncertainty and Learning

In this section we discuss some important technical issues that arise in the implementation of adaptive management, in particular the treatment of uncertainty in resource management and the influence of long-term (and uncertain) environmental trends. We also address attributes of models and management alternatives that promote learning.

4.1. Components of Uncertainty

Here we revisit the components of uncertainty that can affect natural resources in the context of thematic areas explored in this guide. We focus on the uncertainty factors highlighted in Section 2, including environmental variation, partial controllability, partial observability, and structural uncertainty. These uncertainties influence natural resources management in different ways and at different points in a resource system (Figure 4.1). Taken separately or in combination, they can limit understanding of resource functions and restrict our ability to identify useful management strategies. The difficulties they introduce vary with the particular ecological situation, but as a rule their potential impacts increase with the scale and complexity of the resource system.

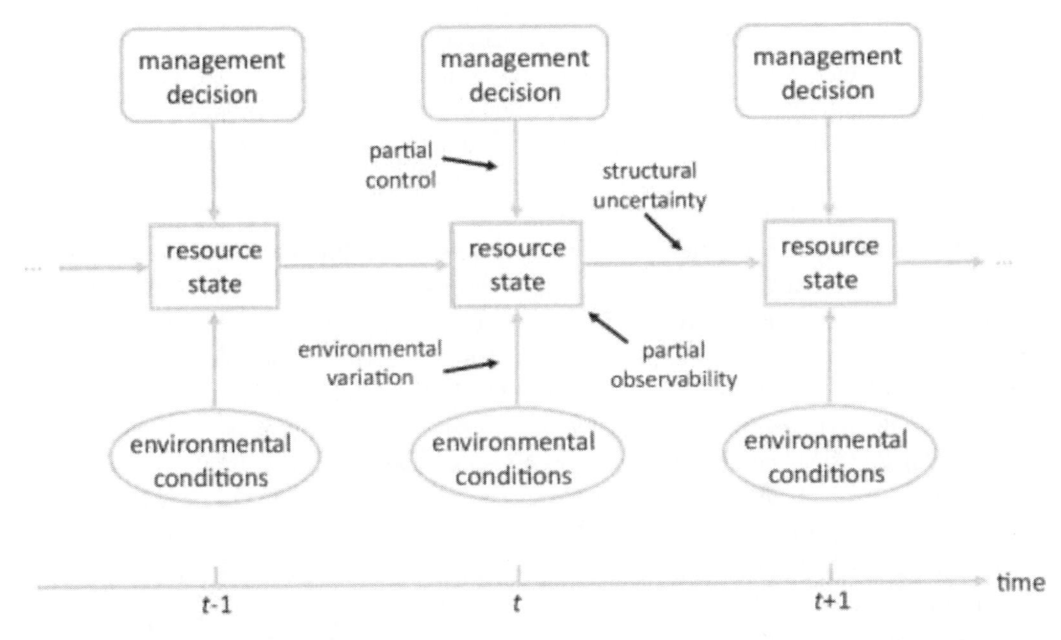

Figure 4.1. Uncertainty factors in natural resource management. Partial control limits the influence of management actions. Environmental variation affects resource system status and dynamics. Partial observability limits the recognition of system status. Structural uncertainty limits the ability to characterize system change.

Environmental variation. Environmental conditions can be viewed as external factors that influence, but are not influenced by, resource conditions and dynamics. Here we consider environmental conditions in terms of the physical environment, as expressed in precipitation patterns, temperature regimes, ambient light conditions and other measures, as well as extremes in these conditions. Environmental conditions directly and indirectly influence the ecological and physical processes that determine resource dynamics. Because they vary randomly over time, future conditions cannot be predicted with certainty.

Environmental fluctuations may be thought of as lacking a discernable pattern of change in central tendency or range of variation. Alternatively, they may be seen in terms of directional trends, such as a long-term decrease in average precipitation or an increase in the range of ambient temperatures. The latter framework is especially relevant to climate change, which is characterized in terms of directional environmental change over an extended period.

Fluctuations in the environment can interact with land-use and land-cover changes that occur during the same time that the climate is changing. Urbanization, deforestation, industrial agriculture, manufacturing, mining, transportation, and other activities have increased worldwide, with potentially profound impacts on resource systems. Because climate change and human development have occurred simultaneously, their impacts are difficult to separate. However, there is little doubt that in combination they are altering natural resource systems and causing long-term changes in resource dynamics.

It often is useful to include unrecognized landscape heterogeneity and unpredictable human impacts on the landscape as a part of "environmental variation." In combination these factors can greatly influence resource responses to management, depending on the scale and unpredictability of the change. For example, management strategies needed for irregular, large-amplitude environmental fluctuations may differ from those needed for more predictable fluctuations of smaller amplitude. Though environmental variation is assumed to be uncontrolled, it can be tracked through monitoring and incorporated into forward-looking management strategies.

Partial controllability. Partial controllability refers to the difference between the results intended by a given management decision and the results that actually occur. Stated formally, it describes a random association between intended and realized management actions. Unintended outcomes are often a result of management decisions implemented by indirect means. For example, hunting permits may be used as an indirect means to attain a chosen rate of waterfowl harvest, as in our example of adaptive harvest management (Section 4.4); or forestry regulations may be used to limit logging-related impacts on wildlife. The net effect is that the intended outcome of a management decision is only partially accomplished by the action taken. One way to account for this is to characterize an anticipated action probabilistically, with a distribution that assigns probabilities of occurrence over a range of potential outcomes.

A somewhat different version of partial controllability can arise if there is a delay between identifying an action and implementing it. In this case partial controllability is induced not by an imprecise or indirect linkage to a control mechanism, but rather by unforeseen circumstances that restrict or prevent the implementation of the action. One example is an unanticipated loss of funds for a management intervention. In such a case there is a point between the identification and implementation of an action when the manager recognizes that the chosen action cannot be carried out.

In actual operations, partial controllability differs from environmental variation in terms of the nature and timing of its effect. Thus, partial controllability occurs at specific points in the resource system where management alters resource conditions and states, with decisions and actions linked at each point in time (Figure 4.1). On the other hand, environmental variation is expressed through fluctuations and trends in environmental conditions over time. Fluctuating environmental conditions influence ecological processes in ways that are uncontrolled, uncertain, and often unrecognized.

Notwithstanding these differences, environmental variation and partial controllability are sometimes combined in models of resource dynamics, mainly because of similarities in the way they are characterized. Like environmental variation, partial controllability increases with geographic scale and ecological complexity: the larger and more complex the resource system, the less certain we can be that management decisions will have the intended outcome. For example, regulations for hunting ungulates may not result in the intended harvest rates if the animals occur in wide-ranging groups (perhaps based on age or sex) with different likelihoods of being seen by hunters.

Partial controllability is likely to cause significant uncertainty in managing projects in the thematic areas emphasized in this guide. For example, indirect mechanisms like tax incentives, permit systems, and carbon trading arrangements may be used to prevent atmospheric carbon dioxide from rising above a certain level, but the net effects of these emissions controls may differ from the outcome that is intended. Climate change adaptation also may involve indirect control mechanisms, such as land transfers, outreach and communication efforts, and regulatory mechanisms. Similarly, partial controllability is likely to be an important uncertainty factor in water management, energy development, and large-scale human activities on the landscape, each of which involves many of the same kinds of management controls that can be used for climate change. The importance of partial controllability varies with scale, and it tends to be less important in localized, smaller-scale projects for which random variation is limited and control can be exercised more directly.

Partial observability. Partial observability expresses our inability to observe completely the resource system that is being managed. Natural resources are almost always partially observed. For example, only a part of the area where a fish population occurs can be monitored, and a sampling strategy needs to allow inferences over the whole area on the basis of the observation of only a part of it. Observability is further complicated by the fact that individuals (e.g., plants and animals) often escape detection, even in areas that are intensively monitored. In combination, incomplete geographic coverage and incomplete detectability mean that observations collected in the field are associated with – but not the same as – actual system states.

Partial observability obscures the resource status on which effective management depends. This reduces management effectiveness, even if environmental variation is minimal and management actions are precisely controlled. For example, decision makers without accurate information can fail to recognize the need to protect a resource, or overlook opportunities for sustainable resource exploitation (Moore and Kendall 2004). These problems become more pronounced under highly variable environmental conditions.

Partial observability is commonly measured by sampling variation, which occurs when field data are collected and analyzed. Unlike environmental variation, over which we have little if any control, the accuracy with which resources are observed can be controlled by designing field sampling efforts efficiently. For example, we can reduce uncertainty about resource status with more intensive sampling, optimal geographic design of the sampling effort, and the use of standard survey principles like randomization, replication, and controls. Nonetheless, partial observability can rarely be eliminated, no matter what the design and sampling intensity.

There are several ways of dealing with partial observability in decision making. One is to estimate resource status with field data, and then treat the estimate as if it accurately represents resource conditions. Another is to state the uncertainty about resource status explicitly, with probabilities for possible resource states, and incorporate these probabilities directly into the decision making process (Williams 2009). The first approach is far more common in natural resource management. Of course, the most direct way to address partial observability is to reduce it as much as is practicable with well-designed monitoring.

Like the other forms of uncertainty, partial observability increases with geographic scale and ecological complexity. For example, wildlife population abundance is more difficult to estimate if populations consist of widely dispersed age or size groups that are not equally detectable. As a general rule, the larger and more complex the resource system, the less certain we can be that the resource estimates on which management is based track the actual system state.

Structural uncertainty. Structural uncertainty is a result of a lack of understanding (or lack of agreement) about the processes that control resource dynamics. In virtually all cases there is some degree of uncertainty about the forms and functions – i.e., the structure – of natural processes. Structural uncertainty can limit our ability to manage resources effectively and efficiently, even if monitoring is exact, management actions are rigorously controlled, and environmental variation is minimal.

The differing views held by stakeholders about how natural processes work and how they respond to management are examples of structural uncertainty. These views can be framed as hypotheses about system processes and responses and then embedded in models, which in turn can be used to make testable predictions. Examples of uncertainty about resource form and function include hypothesized associations between different attributes of the resource, or relationships between controls and resource elements, or connections between environmental conditions and resource states, or parameterizations of these relationships. The hypothesized forms and parameterizations can be incorporated in different models, and structural uncertainty then is expressed in terms of uncertainty about which model (and its embedded hypothesis) best represents resource dynamics.

In adaptive decision making, structural uncertainty changes over time because it is based on evolving resource conditions and management actions. These changes are quantified with measures of confidence in the ability of the models to predict resource dynamics. A common mathematical approach is Bayesian updating, which combines confidence values and monitoring data at each point in time to generate new confidence values for the next point in time (Lee 1989). Confidence increases in models that make accurate forecasts of resource conditions, and confidence declines in models that do not make accurate forecasts. Of course, changes in confidence differ from a change in the hypotheses themselves, which occurs through the process of double-loop learning (see Section 2.7).

Structural uncertainty, like the other forms of uncertainty, has a tendency to obscure the effects of management and reduce effectiveness. However, it differs from environmental variation and partial controllability in its point of influence (Figure 4.1) and the manner in which it is treated. Structural uncertainty can be reduced by applying management strategies to affect the measures of confidence in models. In contrast, environmental variation (and in some cases partial controllability) are effectively uncontrolled.

4.2. Systemic Resource Changes over Time

Adaptive management is usually framed in terms of an (often unstated) assumption that the features and processes of a resource system are stable over the management time frame, so that uncontrolled fluctuations change little in overall direction or range of variation. A generic model for adaptive management assumes that at any given time, resource change is influenced by the state of the resource, environmental conditions, and the management action taken at that time (Figure 2.1). Randomness in environmental conditions induces random resource changes, and directionality in these conditions over time means that uncontrolled resource dynamics also tend to exhibit directionality over time. Conversely, random and non-directional environmental fluctuations tend to preserve dynamic stationarity in resource behaviors. Approaches to system analysis and control, including the framework typically used in adaptive decision making, have traditionally rested on the assumption that system features and patterns of fluctuation are stable over time.

It is becoming increasingly clear that for a great many resource systems, the ecological structures and processes controlling resource dynamics are changing in ways not fully expressed by the management framework depicted in Figure 2.1. Of particular importance is that environmental conditions, and the ecological processes influenced by them, are exhibiting directional patterns of change. An obvious example is climate change, in which the environment is seen as evolving directionally in terms of temperature, precipitation, and other variables.

An important challenge for an adaptive approach is to include directional trends in the environment. Such an extended framework is especially relevant to climate change, as expressed in terms of directional environmental change like a long-term decrease in average precipitation or an increase in the range of ambient temperatures. Of course, directional change can be important over shorter periods as well; many anthropogenic forces exhibit large-scale directional change on shorter time scales than climate change. In either case, directional change has the potential to induce directionality in resource behaviors, i.e., to generate non-stationary resource dynamics.

Non-stationary dynamics become especially challenging for a forward-looking, learning-based approach like adaptive management. Learning about resource processes and management impacts proceeds through an iterative process of decision making, follow-up monitoring, and assessment of impacts. The cycle of learning becomes more difficult when the subjects of investigation – the ecological processes that determine resource change – are themselves evolving.

One way to address this problem is to track and even model the environmental drivers of change, and to use trends in environmental conditions to account for changes in patterns of resource change over time.

Another way is to look for limited periods during which resource processes are largely stable so that learning-based management can be effective. A third approach is to develop environmental scenarios with different patterns of directional change, and try to design acceptable management strategies that account for uncertainties among the scenarios. Adaptive decision making then can be used to address uncertainty about which scenario is appropriate (and therefore which strategy should be chosen).

Non-stationarity is a newly recognized and serious challenge to adaptive decision making, one for which we need new approaches that go beyond the standard ways of framing and conducting learning-based management. At a minimum it is necessary to look for directional trends in environmental conditions and systematic changes in resource structures and functions, and consider ways to accommodate them.

Finally, it is worth re-emphasizing that systemic change in resource dynamics can also be caused by large-scale, effectively permanent human interventions on the landscape. At a certain scale the human footprint on the landscape can be thought of as part of the external environment, and long-term growth of that footprint can easily cause changes in physical and ecological processes. Because it is the result of human actions, the footprint presumably is partially controllable. However, long-term changes, driven in large part by the growth of human populations, economic growth, technological change, and demands for natural resources and space, are unlikely to stabilize in the foreseeable future. Like the directional change in environmental conditions caused by climate change, long-term patterns of increasing resource use and disturbance, and the directional trends they cause in resource dynamics, will need to be taken into account in adaptive decision making.

4.3. Models, Management Alternatives and Learning

In an adaptive management application, both models and management alternatives are identified and agreed upon by managers and other stakeholders. The models, which embed different hypotheses about how the resource system works, represent uncertainty (or disagreement) about ecological processes and the influence of management on them. The management alternatives express a range of potential actions that can be taken at each decision point.

Models play a key role in adaptive management by incorporating different hypotheses about how a resource system works and how it responds to management. Agreements, disagreements, and uncertainties about resource behaviors can be highlighted with models and used to guide investigations through basic research and learning-oriented management interventions.

The management alternatives also play a key role. The identification of informative and effective strategies depends upon differences in predicted responses to management actions. For optimal management, distinctly different predictions should be produced for the alternative actions, so as to facilitate the identification of an optimal action. To promote learning, distinctly different predictions should be produced by the alternative models.

These conditions suggest two ways that adaptive decision making can be compromised. One way is that the models representing uncertainty about system structure produce similar predictions for the alternative actions. Under these circumstances there is little practical value in resolving uncertainty about how the system works, since the models describing system performance all perform equally well. The other way adaptive decision making can be compromised is that the available actions produce essentially indistinguishable results for each model. In this situation there is little value in attempting to discriminate among management alternatives because they all produce similar results. The latter situation often occurs when the potential management alternatives differ only marginally.

This implies that the models and management alternatives should be considered in combination. For a given set of actions, the various models under consideration should predict distinctly different outcomes, so that learning through management becomes possible. Similarly, the various alternatives should produce distinctly different predictions, so that the best action can be clearly seen. Adaptive decision making works best when (*i*) there is substantial variation in the hypothesized forms and functions for the resource system, and (*ii*) management alternatives differ substantively in their predicted resource responses.

A special case of adaptive decision making treats the management alternatives themselves as hypotheses (Williams 2011*a*). Each alternative is seen as a hypothesis about the effectiveness of the action, much as hypotheses in experiments are expressed in terms of responses to experimental treatments (Graybill 1976). The emphasis here is restricted to system responses to management, rather than improved understanding of the ecological processes behind those responses.

As an example, consider the alternatives of clear cutting, thinning, and selective cutting as hypotheses about the best way to manage a forest stand. A choice of one of the alternatives sets up an "experiment," which provides evidence that either does or does not support the intervention as an effective management action. If the forest's response contributes to meeting the management objectives, the intervention is a viable candidate for continued use. A response differing from what was expected or desired suggests that the intervention should be rejected in favor of another. The problem, of course, is that there is always uncertainty about system responses to management interventions, and predictions about the responses must somehow account for those uncertainties. Without a mechanism for learning based on the comparison of alternative predictions against observed evidence, this "experimental" approach can easily become a form of trial and error management.

There are at least two ways to strengthen the inferences of such "experimentation." A traditional way is to use randomization, replication, and controls, when possible, in the spirit of experimental design. Thus, we might use simultaneous interventions on different management units in different places. This makes it possible to compare the effect of one intervention on a group of management units against a different intervention on other units. Our example of post-wildfire management after the Biscuit Fire in Oregon describes such a management study by the Forest Service. Standard statistical treatments can be used for the comparison, with results that can contribute to improved management.

If the interventions are carried out sequentially, one can compare monitoring data against predictions for each alternative to update confidence in the alternatives over time. In this case, one must describe a predicted response to a given intervention under each of the alternative models. For example, hypotheses (models) can be formulated based on the relative responses to clear cutting, selective cutting, and thinning. One common method is to identify confidence values for the intervention models and update these values at each decision point by comparing predicted responses with post-decision monitoring data (Williams et al. 2002). In this way the confidence values can evolve over time, increasing for alternatives that are supported by the data and decreasing for alternatives that are not. A change in the confidence values then becomes a measure of learning over time, leading gradually to recognition of the best intervention.

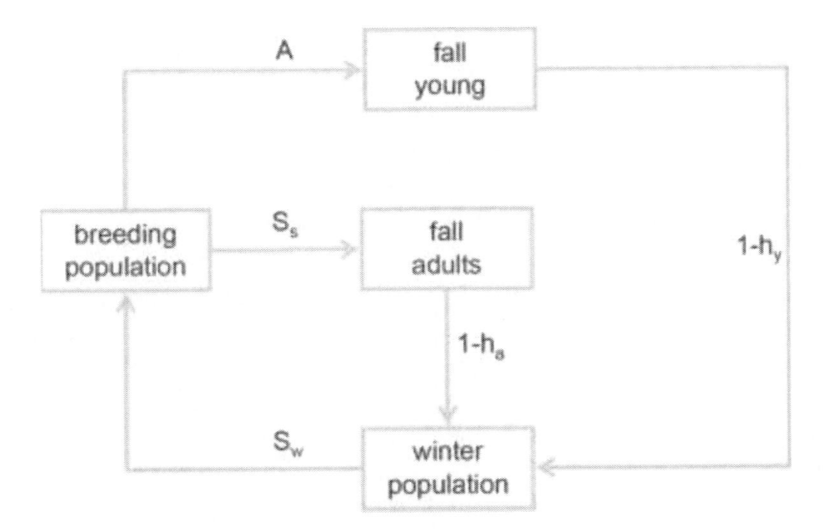

Figure 4.2. Conceptual model of annual cycle of mallard population dynamics. Model includes survival rates for spring-summer (S_s) and fall-winter (S_w), along with harvest rates for young (h_y) and adults (h_a) and age ratio (A) for reproduction/recruitment.

Learning through experimentation typically involves the use of classical hypothesis testing, in which interventions are considered experimental "treatments" and analysis-of-variance methods are used to recognize statistically significant treatment effects. When interventions are implemented sequentially, a popular alternative for learning is to update the credibility of different hypotheses over time on the basis of post-decision monitoring data.

4.4. Example: Uncertainty and Learning in Waterfowl Management

An example that highlights many of the points in this section is the framework for adaptive harvest management of waterfowl. Adaptive harvest management was begun in 1995 as a process for setting annual regulations for the sport hunting of waterfowl in North America (Williams and Johnson 1995, Williams et al. 2002). It uses a simple model to represent associations among fall harvest, seasonal survivorship, and spring reproduction (Figure 4.2). Contrasting hypotheses about the impact of harvest on annual survivorship are easily incorporated into different versions of the model by describing different functional relations between harvest rates and post-harvest survival. In addition, contrasting hypotheses about the importance of density dependence in recruitment are incorporated by describing recruitment in terms of spring population size. In combination, these hypotheses define different models, each with its own predictions about harvest impacts and each with its own measure of confidence that evolves over time. The models and their measures of confidence characterize structural uncertainty, which is reduced as harvest actions are taken and post-harvest monitoring data are used to update the confidence measures. Learning is expressed through the updating of these measures and is folded into the annual process of setting hunting regulations.

The forms of uncertainty we have described in this section enter naturally into this problem. For example, harvest rates that are targeted through the use of regulations result in partial controllability. Environmental variation affects recruitment through water conditions on the breeding grounds, as measured by the abundance of ponds. The change in pond numbers each year is based on the number in the current year and the amount of precipitation the next winter and following spring. Precipitation amounts are assumed to be random and independent from year to year, with no long-term trend in the average amount or severity of precipitation events. Finally, one of the most comprehensive monitoring programs for wildlife in the world (Martin et al. 1979, Smith et al. 1982) is used to estimate the status of waterfowl populations and the parameters that control waterfowl population dynamics.

The assumption of dynamic stability underlies the approach currently used to identify optimal harvest regulations in the presence of the various sources of uncertainty. Thus, harvest strategies are assessed in the context of a dynamic but stable resource system. It is straightforward to incorporate non-stationarity in the waterfowl harvest problem simply by including directionality in the amount of precipitation over time. Long-term directionality in annual precipitation induces systemic changes in the average pond conditions, which in turn induce long-term patterns of change in waterfowl populations and harvests. Under these circumstances the structures and processes of the resource system change through time, even in the absence of harvest. These changes should be taken into account as we evaluate forward-looking harvest strategies (Nichols et al. 2010).

5. Components of the Set-Up Phase of Adaptive Management

In this section and the next we draw upon our case studies to illustrate the elements and processes of adaptive management in the areas of climate change, water, energy, and human impacts on the landscape. We concentrate on these themes for several reasons. They represent major issues and management challenges for the Department of the Interior and the nation at large. Each of the areas comprises a large collection of management challenges, with diverse stakeholders, complex interactions among physical, ecological, and social components, varying levels of uncertainty, and many opportunities for an adaptive approach. Finally, it is easy to see how management problems in each thematic area could benefit from adaptive decision making.

First, we revisit the elements in the set-up or deliberative phase of adaptive management (stakeholder involvement, objectives, management alternatives, predictive models, and monitoring protocols). Summary descriptions of the examples used here are found in the appendix.

5.1. Stakeholder Involvement

Stakeholders bring different perspectives, preferences, and values to decision making. Managers can strengthen their decision making by involving stakeholders in framing a decision problem, identifying its objectives and models, and even developing and implementing monitoring protocols. It is important to have at least some stakeholder engagement in all the set-up elements of a project, and to continue that engagement throughout the project.

Stakeholder involvement varies greatly in the thematic areas considered here. In fact, adaptive decision making does not prescribe how many stakeholders are appropriate, who they should be, or how they should be organized. In some cases a few managers and decision makers may work directly with each other and the resource. In other cases a large number of stakeholders, including managers, scientists, regulatory organizations, private citizens, and others may interact in a highly structured and organized way.

It is not unusual for stakeholders to have widely divergent viewpoints about managing a resource. A critical challenge is to find common ground that will promote decision making despite disagreements about what actions to take and why. Failure to engage important stakeholders, and disagreement about how to frame a resource problem and identify its objectives and management alternatives, are common stumbling blocks. The challenges become more difficult with larger and more complex ecological problems that involve multiple stakeholders and a high degree of uncertainty (or disagreement) about how to value and manage the resource.

As with any endeavor that involves working with groups of people, principles and tools from the social sciences are needed (Endter-Wada et al. 1998, Heller and Zavaleta 2009). Failure to address social dynamics among stakeholders in a participatory process can set a project up for failure long before the advantages of adaptive decision making can be realized.

Climate change. Landscape-scale climate change projects are just now emerging in the United States, and associated stakeholder groups are evolving. Because of the large scale of climate change and the magnitude of its potential consequences, climate change projects are likely to attract numerous stakeholders with strongly held views about the issues and the best approach to climate change mitigation and adaptation. Ensuring that stakeholder perspectives and opinions are heard and considered in strategy framing and implementation is a major concern.

The number of stakeholders could vary, from only a few for a local project involving a nature preserve, to a great many for regional projects involving multiple jurisdictions and management alternatives with wide-ranging impacts. Stakeholder groups will include federal, state, local, and tribal partners if the management options and resources involve their authorities. Stakeholders will be concerned about climate change risks, long-term sustainability of ecosystems and communities, and potential costs of mitigation and adaptation. The complexity of the issues, as well as the values and desires of stakeholders, calls for careful planning and engagement, often in a structured context of facilitated meetings and ongoing communications.

Water resources. Stakeholder interests are tied to the many uses of water. Demand for water almost always exceeds availability, and this creates conditions for potential conflicts. For many projects a broad geographic area is affected by water management. The broader the area, the more likely it is to encompass many different stakeholder perspectives and commitments to specific water uses. For example, a river hydropower project can have an impact on natural resources both upstream and downstream of the dam, with numerous affected parties demanding to be recognized and engaged. The result is a complex milieu of stakeholder interests and the potential for conflict.

For all but the most localized examples, federal and state interests are involved in the adaptive management of water resources. Municipalities often have an interest in lakes and other standing water bodies for drinking water and other uses. Electric utilities, agriculture, recreation interests, and conservationists are almost always key stakeholders in the adaptive management of rivers and reservoirs for hydropower. Again, the high level of complexity means that stakeholder involvement needs to be well planned, and perhaps facilitated.

Energy. Adaptive management projects are beginning to deal with established renewable technologies such as solar and wind power, with emerging renewable energy technologies such as wave power a step behind. The possibility of contention is likely to be high if the area covered by a project is large and the devices (e.g., underwater turbines, floating buoy-like devices, etc.) have the potential to affect protected species or local livelihoods. With more traditional energy projects involving fossil fuels (e.g., oil and gas), there are usually large numbers of active stakeholders, especially if species of interest or public lands are affected.

Stakeholders in energy projects usually include federal permitting and regulatory agencies such as the Bureau of Land Management and the Fish and Wildlife Service, along with state agencies, environmental groups, industry, recreational users, ranchers, and local citizens. There are often conflicting views about the importance of different management objectives like endangered species survival and economic return from extractive operations. Two core issues are the siting of new energy facilities and the operation of existing facilities.

Because energy production is a strategic goal of DOI, stakeholder interactions must be facilitated in ways that lessen potential conflicts over these issues.

Human/natural interface. As with the previous themes, the diversity and complexity of stakeholder groups can lead to multiple management objectives in apparent conflict, and in turn to conflicts among stakeholders. Single-agency projects with one or a few objectives (e.g., management of a single species of high concern) generally have fewer stakeholders and less potential for conflict. As the geographic scope of a project expands, so too does the universe of concerned parties. In small areas managed by a single agency or landowner (e.g., water management on a refuge wetland), project activities may have no effect on interests outside the project. Projects with a larger geographic and ecological scope probably involve a larger number of parties with their own perspectives and special interests; these projects need structured approaches for getting stakeholders involved.

Examples of stakeholder involvement

Laysan duck translocation and sea level rise

The Laysan duck is an endangered species with breeding sites so restricted that any catastrophe, such as sea-level rise due to climate change, could result in extinction. To increase chances of species survival, managers from the Fish and Wildlife Service and the National Oceanic and Atmospheric Administration are preparing to manage the translocation of ducks adaptively in order to establish breeding populations on other unoccupied islands within the Papahānaumokuākea Marine National Monument, northwestern Hawaiian islands. Stakeholders include the National Oceanic and Atmospheric Administration, the Fish and Wildlife Service, the U.S. Geological Survey, and Hawaiian state agencies, all of which share a primary objective of endangered species recovery. If translocation extends into the main Hawaiian islands, public meetings and outreach to further stakeholders may be needed.

Glen Canyon Dam

The Glen Canyon Dam on the Colorado River was authorized by Congress in 1956 and constructed in the late 1950s by the Bureau of Reclamation for the primary purposes of water storage and hydroelectric power production. Dam operations fundamentally altered the river ecosystem, and concerns related to impacts on downstream riparian ecosystems, recreation, and endangered species, particularly native fish, were driving forces for change in the operation of Glen Canyon Dam. After completion of an environmental impact statement required by the Grand Canyon Protection Act of 1992, the Secretary of the Interior approved the initiation of the Glen Canyon Dam Adaptive Management Program. The program brought together a broad spectrum of stakeholders with widely divergent views on river management under the framework and structure of the Federal Advisory Committee Act. The stakeholder group consists of 25 members including federal and state agencies, Native American tribes, the Colorado River basin states, hydropower distributors and users, and recreational and environmental interests. The program makes recommendations to the Secretary of the Interior, and uses scientific investigations, experimental actions, and adaptive management principles to help inform recommendations about dam operations and other actions. The continuing focus of the program is to ensure that Colorado River flow regimes from Glen

Canyon Dam meet the goals of supplying water for communities, agriculture, and industry and providing clean hydropower in a manner that protects the downstream resources as required by the Grand Canyon Protection Act of 1992.

Blanca wetlands

The Blanca wetlands site is a complex of shallow and deep ponds, marshes, and wetland systems managed by the Bureau of Land management in Colorado's San Luis Valley. It is maintained through a series of artesian wells, irrigation canals, and diversion ditches. Because of the relatively small scale of adaptive management in the Blanca wetlands, only limited stakeholder involvement is currently necessary. The Bureau of Land Management has partnered with the Colorado Division of Wildlife, the Fish and Wildlife Service, and Ducks Unlimited to restore and preserve habitats in the area. Bureau staff meet annually with a wetlands focus group that includes representatives of other agencies to identify priorities and issues associated with water availability and species needs in the larger wetland complex in the valley.

Wyoming Landscape Conservation Initiative

The ongoing development of public lands in southwest Wyoming for coal, oil, natural gas, and uranium since the late 19th century affects wildlife species such as the sage grouse, a candidate for federal listing as an endangered species, and wildlife habitats. The Wyoming Landscape Conservation Initiative was launched in 2007 to conserve and enhance wildlife habitat in areas of oil, gas, and other resource development. Stakeholders include federal agency collaborators such as the Bureau of Land Management, the U.S. Geological Survey, and the Forest Service, along with state agencies, counties, and other government organizations. Non-governmental organizations include environmental and recreation groups, as well as industry and landowner representatives.

Adaptive management of waterfowl harvests

Adaptive harvest management was developed to deal with uncertainties in the regulation of sport waterfowl hunting in North America. Early each year, the Fish and Wildlife Service announces its intent to establish waterfowl hunting regulations and provides the schedule of public rule-making. The agency director appoints a Migratory Bird Regulations Committee that presides over the process and is responsible for regulatory recommendations. The committee convenes public meetings during summer to review biological information and to consider proposals from regulations consultants, who represent the flyway councils. The flyway councils and the state fish and wildlife agencies they represent are essential partners in the management of migratory bird hunting. After deliberations by the committee and regulations consultants, the Service presents hunting-season proposals at public hearings and in the *Federal Register* for comment. Through this formal process, interested stakeholders have an opportunity each year to express their opinions and recommendations about harvest regulations and potential impacts on waterfowl populations.

Las Cienegas National Conservation Area

The Las Cienegas National Conservation Area in northern Arizona was once the historic Empire and Cienega ranches. The Sonoita Valley Planning Partnership (SVPP) was formed in 1995 to help the Bureau of Land Management develop a land-use plan covering both commercial grazing interests and ecosystem conservation. The participants include individuals from more than a dozen communities in southern Arizona, conservation groups such as The Nature Conservancy and Arizona Zoological Society, graziers, recreational user groups, and multiple federal, state, and other governmental organizations. SVPP and other partners work with the Bureau of Land Management on conservation area management and protection of buffer lands around the area.

Everglades floodplain wetland management

The 57,800-hectare A.R.M. Loxahatchee National Wildlife Refuge is a floodplain wetland at the northern end of the remaining Florida Everglades. This refuge is surrounded by 280,000 hectares of farmland on one side and residential areas for 6.5 million people on the other. The refuge serves a triple purpose of providing flood protection, water, and wildlife habitat (numerous threatened and endangered species, migratory birds, and other trust resources rely on refuge habitat). Refuge managers work with three major stakeholders at the federal, state, and local level: the U.S. Army Corps of Engineers, the South Florida Water Management District, and the Lake Worth Drainage District. These partners collectively manage water levels within the refuge to follow an established water regulation schedule, which comprises a set of operational rules for moving water into and out of the wetland on the basis of water levels in the marsh and the time of year. Refuge staff and managers use a variety of communication fora to exchange information relevant to water management actions.

Fire fuel treatments in the Sierra Nevada

Millions of hectares of forest in California are at risk from wildfires, and controversial management of fire fuels on Forest Service lands in the Sierra Nevada has generated disagreements and lawsuits since 1990. To help reconcile conflicts over fire fuels management, an adaptive management project is being used to implement the 2004 Sierra Nevada Forest Plan Amendment. The 7-year project evaluates how different forest vegetation treatments can slow fire spread and reduce fire intensity, within the constraints of maintaining water quality, habitat for the Pacific fisher and California spotted owl, and residential safety. Stakeholders include federal representatives from Forest Service regional offices, national forests, the Forest Service's Pacific Southwest Research Station, and the Fish and Wildlife

Service; representatives from several state agencies such as CalFire and the California Department of Fish and Game; and a university science team with members from several University of California branches and the University of Minnesota.

5.2. Objectives

Successful implementation of adaptive management depends on a clear statement of project objectives, defined here as intended outcomes or performance measures to guide decision making and recognize success. Objectives represent benchmarks against which to compare the potential effects of different management actions. They also serve as measures to evaluate the effectiveness of management strategies, and they contribute to the reduction of uncertainty over time. Objectives influence the operation of adaptive management so much, and in so many ways, that it is unclear how adaptive decision making can happen without them.

Objectives in adaptive management often target particular goals or end results – for example, achieving a restoration goal. Some objectives are stated in terms of optimization – for example, maximizing long-term biological harvest or minimizing long-term costs of ecological recovery. Others involve specific criteria – for example, meeting a set of resource and management conditions. In all cases, objectives should be consistent with legal and regulatory requirements.

With large numbers of stakeholders there are usually multiple objectives, some of which may be in conflict. For example, objectives for a water release project might include the use of water for agriculture, power generation, recreation, and ecological sustainability, with the recognition that available water is insufficient to meet all these demands. Constraints imposed by agency-specific legal or regulatory requirements can lead to conflict among stakeholders and their objectives. The different missions of agencies can also create contention. Incorporating multiple values and measures adds complexity to the task of identifying objectives. Under these circumstances it is important to consider tradeoffs among potential objectives.

As mentioned in Section 1, adaptive management facilitates not only technical learning about ecological processes, but also institutional learning about management objectives and other adaptive management components. Double-loop learning gives an opportunity to reconsider project objectives over time, so they can be adjusted as needed when the resource changes or when stakeholder values and perspectives change. Double-loop learning is discussed in more detail in Section 2.7 and Section 6.

Climate change. For climate change projects, objectives will fall into two broad categories: (*i*) mitigation of climate change by reducing or eliminating its causes (primarily by reducing emissions of greenhouse gases or sequestering carbon); and (*ii*) adaptation to the consequences of climate change. Reducing impacts on resources and buffering ecological processes and systems will be typical objectives. Because of deep uncertainties about the magnitude, timing, and even direction of climate change and resource responses, a special effort must be made to ensure that adaptive management objectives are meaningful, achievable, agreed upon by stakeholders, and relevant over time. Climate-induced changes in environmental conditions will complicate the process of setting management objectives by altering resource processes and dynamics in unpredictable ways (Williams and Jackson 2007, Knutson and Heglund 2011). The uncertainties surrounding climate change underscore the importance of maintaining the capacity to adjust project objectives and to learn quickly as climate patterns are revealed over time.

Water resources. Most water resources can be used in diverse ways for multiple objectives. It is important to reach agreement on objectives, how to weight them, and how to account for the possibility of revising them over time as evidence about the resource system accumulates and stakeholder values evolve. Reconciling conflicting demands for limited water (such as dam releases to accommodate peak electricity demand versus flow regimes to maintain native fauna and flora downstream) requires compromise on initial objectives that can be refined and revised later through the process of double-loop learning.

Energy. Obvious measures of importance in setting objectives are the amount and timing of energy production, though these measures sometimes serve as constraints in the framework of a project rather than objectives. Other important measures include impacts on the landscape from the siting of facilities, disturbance from infrastructure development (e.g., roads, power lines), ecological impacts from facilities operations, and the consequences of energy production for social and economic conditions in the area.

Human/natural interface. Here, objectives may include goals to be attained within some time limit, minimization of management costs, maximization of resource benefits, and tradeoffs among multiple objectives to achieve acceptable levels of performance for each. For example, one might seek to minimize ecological damage (e.g., from pests) as well as the cost of management, or to maximize ecological attributes (e.g., a viable wildlife population that can accommodate sport hunting) as well as ecological processes (e.g., reproduction on the breeding grounds).

Examples of management objectives

Glen Canyon Dam

The Glen Canyon Dam on the Colorado River was constructed by the Bureau of Reclamation for the primary purposes of water storage and hydroelectric power production. Public concerns regarding adverse impacts of dam operations on downstream resources, including endangered native fish, led to changes in dam operations and passage of the 1992 Grand Canyon Protection Act. The Glen Canyon Dam Adaptive Management Program was adopted to meet requirements in the Grand Canyon Protection Act. The program's objectives express stakeholders' views and priorities regarding the operation of Glen Canyon Dam and other related activities. Glen Canyon Dam is operated under applicable federal law, including the Law of the Colorado River and the direction provided by Congress in 1992 to operate the dam in a manner that protects, mitigates adverse impacts on, and improves the values for which Grand Canyon National Park and Glen Canyon National Recreation Area were established, including but not limited to natural and cultural resources and visitor use.

Offshore wind farm on the Atlantic coast

Offshore wind facilities may occupy as much as 65 square kilometers or more of ocean, with turbines over half a kilometer apart. Turbines typically are installed on a hard substrate, and are connected by cables to a service platform. Concerns relate to fisheries and boating recreation in the vicinity, as well as possible impacts on bats, birds, and marine life. In deciding where to site such a wind facility, objectives to maximize energy production and minimize costs are weighed against objectives to minimize impacts on important trust species, maintain fish and shellfish harvests, and minimize impacts on marine transport and recreation in coastal areas.

Predator control at Cape Lookout National Seashore

Human activity at Cape Lookout National Seashore has led to an increasing raccoon population and an increase in predation of shorebird nests. Reducing the raccoon population can help to meet the objective of increasing shorebird reproductive success, within the constraint of the park's larger mandate to preserve all native species at viable levels. An adaptive approach to managing predator abundance has been developed to (*i*) minimize the number of raccoons removed, (*ii*) keep the raccoon population above a minimum threshold, and (*iii*) increase oystercatcher productivity above a set threshold.

Cape Cod National Seashore wind turbines

The Cape Cod National Seashore plans to install several wind turbines to reduce greenhouse gas emissions from park facilities, as part of its mission to serve as a regional model of environmental sustainability. Objectives focus on maximizing wind power within the constraints of protecting birds and bats. If negative impacts on fauna are found to be unavoidable, alternate renewable energy sources (e.g., solar) will be considered.

Adaptive harvest management

Adaptive harvest management was developed to deal with uncertainties in the regulation of sport waterfowl hunting in North America. The Migratory Bird Treaty Act of 1918 (as amended) authorizes establishment of annual hunting regulations for migratory birds. Managers try to maximize the value of long-term cumulative harvest, with an implicit goal of sustainability. Harvest value has been defined as a function of harvest and other performance metrics. For mid-continent mallards, managers want to maximize long-term cumulative harvest; the annual harvest is weighted proportionally less if population size is expected to fall below the goal set by the North American Waterfowl Management Plan. Defining harvest value in this way decreases the likelihood of population sizes below the plan's goal. An additional constraint on long-term harvest potential eliminates consideration of closed seasons as long as predicted population size is at least 5.5 million.

Columbia River chinook salmon

Numerous dams have been established on the Columbia River for hydropower, irrigation, and flood control, but they have adverse impacts on native fish and have negatively affected spawning and recruitment of fall-run chinook salmon. Public utility districts of the middle Columbia River work with federal and state agencies and Native American tribes to set priorities for power generation and fish and wildlife protection. Dam relicensing by the Federal Energy Regulatory Commission highlighted the need to protect chinook spawning areas in the Hanford Reach of the Columbia. An adaptive management working group representing the stakeholders established a procedure for water releases to minimize the risk that chinook breeding areas would dry out from water fluctuations in the river, within the constraint of meeting energy demands. To achieve this objective, maximum and minimum daytime flow rates during the fall spawning season were needed to limit spawning at high elevations (which dry out as water levels drop), while at the same time retaining enough water on the lower spawning areas to allow successful spawning.

5.3. Management Alternatives

Adaptive decision making requires the clear identification of a set of potential alternatives from which to select an action at each decision point. Some actions might affect the resource directly – for example, harvest, stocking, or habitat alteration. On the other hand, actions might have indirect effects – for example, regulations to limit overuse. A set of potential actions might consist of different levels of a single type of action, such as a range of harvest rates. Alternatively, the set might include actions of different kinds, such as predator control, understory thinning, and recreational use.

Learning and decision making both depend on our ability to recognize differences in the consequences of different actions. Selecting potential actions that have distinctly different consequences offers the possibility of comparing and contrasting them in order to choose the best one.

Climate change. Potential management actions for climate change range widely, from regulation of resource use, to physical alteration of ecosystems and ecological processes, to translocation of species. Actions can be expressed in terms of broad strategies implemented over an extended time, or limited interventions aimed at particular resource issues. Management strategies can be designed to respond to changeable climatic conditions as well as changeable resource states. For example, a particular strategy for climate adaptation or mitigation might be designed specifically for one particular climate change scenario, but not for others. For any given project, the challenge will be to identify a useful set of climate scenarios, link them to relevant management options, and decide on a particular option.

Water resources. Management alternatives for water resources often involve controls on water inputs, outputs, and allocation for competing uses. Other management options include actions that focus on maintaining or improving water quality, or retaining water in order to control floods. Management strategies can involve direct controls (e.g., releasing specific amounts of water for wetlands or river management) or indirect controls (e.g., regulating runoff of agricultural chemicals into streams).

Energy. Management alternatives for energy projects can be divided conveniently into (*i*) decisions about siting of new facilities, (*ii*) decisions about the development of supporting infrastructure (roads, power lines, pipelines), and (*iii*) decisions about the operation of facilities (timing and amount of energy production). A particular project might include any combination of these management elements.

Human/natural interface. For biological and ecological systems, management alternatives may have direct effects on the resource state, or on processes and vital rates such as mortality, reproduction, or migration. Management actions can also have indirect effects – for example, regulatory actions can restrict resource use through permits, quotas, license sales, etc. Management options might also focus on organism growth, population management, habitat alteration, control of human disturbance, and similar interventions.

Examples of management alternatives

Blanca wetlands

The Blanca Wildlife Habitat Area in southern Colorado encompasses over 6,200 hectares of marshes, ponds, and periodically flooded basins called playas, which provide habitat for a wide variety of wildlife and plant species. The management plan for the area emphasizes its use by waterfowl, shorebirds, and amphibians. The Bureau of Land Management manages habitat with artesian water, canals, and diversion ditches, and annually adjusts seasonal habitat availability for particular species groups. Periodic flooding of playas produces high densities of insects and vegetation critical to wetland birds. Periodic drying of large wetland basins is also important in order to mimic the natural hydrology that supports ecological processes such as plant succession. Each year, managers release water from artesian wells into freshwater marshes and ponds. The amount and timing of water released are chosen each season from a range of possible alternatives related to annual water quality objectives, as well as provision of sufficient irrigated wetland areas to compensate for whatever basins are undergoing periodic drying. These habitat manipulations affect waterfowl, shorebird, and amphibian populations, which are the ultimate management targets.

Solar project siting and permitting

In California, proposed industry-grade solar energy projects range in size from 200 to 3,200 hectares, and may have a major impact on natural resources. The land and resources within a project boundary are affected by the placement of solar collectors, development of service roads, and mowing of vegetation. Wells may be dug at a site to obtain the water needed to wash the collectors regularly. In addition, rainwater retention basins may be developed, which can interfere with desert sand transport cycles. Because flat terrain is necessary, projects are often built on valley floors and thus can affect nearby alluvial fans. An adaptive management application for a permit system for solar energy development might use systematic implementation and evaluation to learn about the best ways to site new projects. For example, a solar farm could be divided into two segments, or sited in an existing brown-field area, or designed as a long thin strip perpendicular to the direction of sand transport. Monitoring the impacts of a particular design at one site could provide information about potential impacts at subsequent sites.

Native prairie restoration in national wildlife refuges

Native prairies in national wildlife refuges on the northern Great Plains are being invaded to varying degrees by plants such as smooth brome and Kentucky bluegrass, the result of decades-long suppression of natural disturbance. By reintroducing disturbance, refuge managers hope to control invasive plants and restore a high proportion of native species. Disturbance treatments directly modify the system state (grazing or haying to remove cover of invasive species) or affect biological process rates (e.g., burning to suppress growth rate of invasive species). Managers choose annually one of five main management alternatives – burn, graze, hay, burn/graze, or rest. For each alternative, there are broad sideboards on timing and intensity.

Endangered mussel translocation

Northern riffleshell mussels, along with many other freshwater mollusks, have disappeared from their former range to such a degree that they are now federally listed as endangered. Translocation is an important means of promoting the recovery of these species. When bridge construction on the Allegheny River resulted in a formal Endangered Species Act consultation with the Fish and Wildlife Service, a mussel relocation program was mandated. The Allegheny riffleshells were translocated to the Big Darby Creek, Ohio, in an effort to augment a small population within the species' historic range. Management alternatives involved interconnected decisions about the number of mollusks to be moved, the genetic and demographic composition of the translocated population, optimal release sites with preferred microhabitats and host fish, methods for minimizing disease transfer, and the season for transfer. Individuals are fitted with miniature transponders to allow the monitoring of translocation success. Information gained from this translocation will be directly applicable to future mussel restoration efforts.

Everglades floodplain wetland management

The interior marsh of the A.R.M. Loxahatchee National Wildlife Refuge is surrounded by a perimeter canal that transports water in and out of the floodplain wetland. The canal carries urban and agricultural storm-water runoff. Although the storm-water has been partially treated to remove excess nutrients, the level of phosphorus is still high. Refuge staff are working with partners to minimize the intrusion of nutrient-rich water into the marsh. Management alternatives consist of different combinations of canal-water inflows and wetland outflows in relation to various water depths. Permanent transects are set up to monitor movement of nutrient-enriched water from the canal into the heart of the wetland.

Five Rivers forest landscape management

The Oregon coastal range forests are some of the most productive in the temperate zone. Forest Service lands in this area were set aside mainly for late-successional and riparian habitat in the Northwest Forest Plan. Questions emerged about how to grow and improve habitat, especially on the existing forest plantations that make up about half the forest area. Collaborations among state and federal agencies and public groups resulted in the development of three management strategies that were included in an environmental impact statement, each thought to be scientifically valid given the uncertainties about achieving objectives. One strategy emphasizes closing roads permanently and allowing natural disturbances to thin stands, while allowing late-successional and riparian habitat to "recover naturally." A second strategy keeps roads open and allows repeated entries to thin plantations and add wood to streams. A third strategy focuses on closing roads after more aggressively thinning stands and aiding riparian habitat, and then reopening roads 30 years later to repeat the cycle. The strategies were implemented on 12 landscape areas of 485 hectares each (three strategies and four replicates) of national forest lands.

Coastal wetland impoundments and potential sea level rise

Many coastal wildlife refuges maintain wetland impoundments to enhance habitat and attract large numbers of shorebirds, waterfowl, and other wildlife. Rising sea level is a threat to these impoundments and their complex dike systems. Adaptive management of impoundments that are threatened by sea level rise might entail management alternatives such as: (*i*) manipulation of hydrology (e.g., by infrastructure improvements) and vegetation to meet current conservation targets; (*ii*) identification of new conservation targets and a new suite of management practices for them; or (*iii*) removal of the infrastructure and restoration of the impoundment to a naturally functioning wetland community. The management actions might consist of direct habitat alteration with different levels of a single type of intervention (such as alterations to dikes), or different types of interventions (such as planting vegetation versus removing infrastructure). The actions would be expected to result in different numbers of waterbirds and wildlife, the resources ultimately targeted by management.

Biscuit Fire landscape management after the wildfire

The Biscuit fire burned about 200,000 hectares in southwestern Oregon. Much controversy surrounded how to respond to the burning of vast areas of late-successional forest. Management strategies were openly debated in major news outlets and included dueling scientists, but official stakeholder input took place according to the National Environmental Policy Act process. An interdisciplinary team proposed a management study that compares three strategies: (*i*) focus on natural succession without salvage logging; (*ii*) salvage dead stands according to forest plan guidelines, then replant Douglas fir and control competing vegetation to grow large trees quickly; and (*iii*) reintroduce prescribed fire and plant more fire-resistant pines after salvaging stands as in the second strategy. These strategies were implemented across 14,568 hectares in 12 landscape areas of 1,214 hectares each (three strategies and four replicates) with some variations because of changes in economics caused by litigative delays. About 3,600 hectares of the study are on Bureau of Land Management lands; the remainder are on national forest lands.

Adaptive harvest management

Adaptive harvest management was developed to deal with uncertainties in the regulation of sport waterfowl hunting in North America. Each year the Fish and Wildlife Service establishes "framework" regulations for waterfowl hunting that are flyway-specific. The frameworks specify the earliest and latest dates for hunting seasons, the maximum number of days in the season, and daily bag and possession limits. States select hunting seasons within the bounds of these frameworks, usually following their own processes for proposals and public comment. With the advent of an adaptive approach to harvest management in 1995, the number of potential frameworks was limited to three, which were characterized as restrictive, moderate, and liberal regulations. These three regulatory frameworks, along with the possibility of a closed season, constitute the management alternatives available during each year's process for setting waterfowl hunting seasons.

Yosemite toads and livestock grazing

The Yosemite toad, an altitudinal endemic amphibian of forests in the Sierra Nevada range, is a candidate species for listing under the Endangered Species Act. Because the toads are associated with shallow water in high montane and subalpine meadows, livestock use of wet meadows may significantly affect toad populations. The U.S. Forest Service is using experimental management to examine the relationship between grazing intensity and toad occupancy in livestock grazing allotments and ungrazed meadows in national forests. The four alternative management treatments are: (*i*) grazing in accordance with current stream-bank disturbance standards across an entire meadow; (*ii*) exclusion of livestock from wet areas within a meadow; (*iii*) no grazing in a meadow; and (*iv*) no grazing in a historically ungrazed meadow. Results will provide recommendations for future livestock grazing management to enhance survival and recruitment of the toad.

Agriculture experimentation

Agriculture provides many examples of experimental management. A typical problem involves uncertainty about which of several agricultural practices (different grains, fertilizers, crop rotation patterns, etc.) can produce higher and more consistent yields in an area. A management design might involve application of different agriculture practices in different fields, with some or all the features of an experiment (i.e., randomization, replication, and controls). Field applications often use randomized or randomized block designs. The process becomes adaptive when the elements of the adaptive management framework are used: objectives are clearly stated, potential outcomes are specified, monitoring protocols are decided, the method of learning is explicit, and the results of the experiment are used to update understanding and guide future agricultural practices.

Fire fuel treatments in the Sierra Nevada

Millions of hectares of forest in California are at risk from wildfires, and management of fire fuels on Forest Service lands in the Sierra Nevada has resulted in decades of controversy. To help reconcile conflicts, an adaptive management project is being used to implement the 2004 Sierra Nevada Forest Plan Amendment. The 7-year project evaluates how different forest vegetation treatments can slow fire spread and reduce fire intensity, within the constraints of maintaining water quality, wildlife habitat, and residential safety. The project involves reduction of fire fuels in a series of patches by use of strategically placed area treatments at the landscape level. Across approximately 17,200 hectares, 1,860 hectares are being considered for treatment alternatives that include (*i*) thinning and biomass removal by tractor, (*ii*) mastication, or (*iii*) prescribed burning. Decisions involve size, location, and intensity of treatments. Within treatments, different silvicultural prescriptions identify the species, size, and spatial arrangement of trees to be removed in order to achieve specified crown spacing, tree density, or canopy cover.

Great Barrier Reef marine reserve management

The Great Barrier Reef is a 2,000-kilometer-long complex of coral reefs and other ecosystems such as coastal seagrass beds and diverse sea-floor habitats covering 350,000 square kilometers off the northeast coast of Australia. A national marine park, it contains the world's largest network of marine reserves, which are designed systematically at a regional scale. Adaptive management is being used to restore ecosystem structure (e.g., widespread recovery of depleted fish stocks) and to prevent ongoing degradation (e.g., reduced coral mortality). The Great Barrier Reef Zoning Plan 2004 focuses on apex predators (reef sharks), commercially fished species (coral trout, redthroat emperor), and species of conservation concern (marine turtles, dugongs). Management incorporates a range of alternatives including spatial management with different levels of zoning (general use areas for trawling and gill-netting; no-trawling areas; limited-fishing areas; no-take areas; and no-entry areas); and within fished zones, nonspatial strategies including fishing gear restrictions (e.g., bycatch reduction and turtle excluder devices) and explicit management of fisheries (e.g., licenses, fish size restrictions, commercial quotas, temporal closures during spawning).

5.4. Predictive Models

Models play a critical role in adaptive management, as expressions of our understanding of the resource, engines of ecological inference, and indicators of the benefits, costs, and consequences of alternative management strategies. Importantly, they can represent uncertainty (or disagreement) about the resource system. In the context of management, models project the consequences of different management interventions over time and help to examine how each management intervention might achieve objectives.

There are few restrictions on the number and kind of models used for adaptive management. However, certain features are required. The models must characterize resource changes over time, as the resource responds to fluctuating environmental conditions and management actions. They should embed hypotheses that are relevant to the management problem. To the extent needed, they should incorporate the forms of uncertainty described earlier. Finally, they must differ in the responses they predict as a result of management, for only then will it be useful for management to clarify which model best describes resource structure and function.

In general, as the scale and complexity of the ecological system and the management problem increase, larger and more complex models are needed to characterize the problem. Complexity and large dimension can be serious challenges to using models effectively. Nonetheless, many of the projects in this guide involve complex features and linkages, as well as many uncertainties in the associations between management and outcomes. These features require thoughtfulness and collaboration in the selection and formulation of models.

Climate change. Climate change can be usefully characterized in terms of external environmental drivers such as temperature and precipitation regimes, wind patterns, cloud cover, etc. These factors are the most immediate expressions of a changing climate, and they can be incorporated as external drivers in resource models. In some cases potential climate variations can be treated as simple hypotheses about the pattern of change and responses of the resource. In other cases climate variations can be expressed as climate scenarios and uncertainties, or incorporated along with management actions into expressions of ecological processes.

The treatment of climate change must involve, either implicitly or explicitly, the characterization of instability (technically, non-stationarity) described in Section 4. Structural changes in natural resource systems are inherited from climate change, along with uncertainties about the size and even the direction of change. One way to incorporate the effect of climate change in modeling is to express different trajectories of the climate drivers (see Figure 4.1) as different climate scenarios.

Because of the scale at which climate change is thought to operate, its impact acts most directly on landscapes, by means of changes in landscape structure and function. Landscape changes in turn provide context for climate-driven changes in ecological relationships. Models can incorporate landform and land-use changes as well as ecological attributes. Structural uncertainty can be expressed as different forms of these patterns of change.

Water resources. A natural modeling framework for water resources is a balance equation that accounts for (*i*) flows into a water body from runoff, subsurface water movement, and drainage from streams and rivers; (*ii*) movement of water out of the water body, due to surface and subsurface drainage and evaporation; (*iii*) attributes of the standing volume of water at any point in time; and (*iv*) ecosystem functions related to water conditions and management. Models of moving water focus on hydrodynamics, characterized by water velocity and other dynamic factors. Hydrodynamic effects on stream and river beds, banks, and riparian zones, and the ecological changes that occur in response, can also be included. Models of standing water bodies incorporate attributes like changes in water volume, nutrient cycling, heat flow and temperature patterns in the water column, water turbidity and quality, and the organisms in the water body. Structural uncertainties are often related to the ecological functions that drive these features.

Energy. Models of energy development and use focus on (*i*) the selection of sites for infrastructure development and (*ii*) the operation of existing energy facilities. The framework for site selection differs somewhat from that for operations. A site, once selected, is developed and remains in place for the indefinite future. Modeling of site selection involves decisions about where to locate future sites on the basis of what is learned from follow-up monitoring of existing sites. Important components of this kind of model include habitat structure and function at potential sites, patterns of habitat fragmentation, and impacts on plants and animals. Structural uncertainties can be represented by different forms of these patterns and processes.

Facility operations at a specific site are seen as an ongoing process that incorporates what has been learned from past operations into ongoing management decision making. Issues of concern for these models include habitat alteration, timing and frequency of disturbances, and impacts of operations on flora and fauna in the area. Again, different forms of these patterns and processes can be used to express structural uncertainties.

Human/natural interface. The very large class of natural resource issues related to this theme covers activities like habitat alterations and stocking or removal of plants and animals across a wide range of geographic and ecological scales. Models can be quite varied, with many different methodological approaches and details of structure and mechanism. Many models focus on the management of individual species or local habitats, while others address much broader issues such as biodiversity or ecosystem integrity. The underlying framework of a balance equation (for energy, mass, or number of organisms) is common. Structural uncertainties are represented by hypothesized forms of the processes that drive resource changes over time.

Like climate change, large-scale human interventions can induce unstable (i.e., non-stationary) resource dynamics. In both cases instability of resource behaviors presents new complications and challenges in modeling natural resource dynamics and formulating forwardlooking strategies.

Examples of models

New England shrub habitats on refuges

Shrub communities on national wildlife refuges in the northeast are important habitats for migrating land birds and the New England cottontail rabbit, a candidate for listing under the Endangered Species Act. Fish and Wildlife Service managers use adaptive management to control the invasive plants that degrade native shrub communities and reduce native stem densities and berries required by rabbits and birds. A key uncertainty is how much effort is needed to restore native shrub communities successfully. Two alternative models are aligned with treatment options that include different combinations of mechanical and chemical controls to reduce invasive plants. The models incorporate different mechanisms of change for key shrub attributes that can influence bird and rabbit populations (e.g., berry density, stem density, community composition), along with predictions about how these attributes will change in response to restoration treatments.

Laysan duck translocation

The Laysan duck is an endangered species so restricted that any catastrophe, such as sea level rise due to climate change, could result in extinction. To increase the chance of its survival, U.S. Geological Survey scientists and Fish and Wildlife Service managers are developing a framework for adaptively managing translocation of ducks in order to establish populations on other islands in the northwestern Hawaiian islands. To consider the potential consequences of different translocation actions, a modeling team is building occupancy models to predict long-term persistence of duck populations. The models are linked to a framework for optimizing management actions on the basis of the resources available for conducting translocation. The models describe important relationships and uncertainties in the system, which include catastrophic events (e.g., tsunamis), disease outbreaks, accidental predator introductions, and habitat limitation or carrying capacity (and its relationship to sea-level rise) as the primary drivers of duck population dynamics. Island areas are classified on the basis of whether or not they are currently occupied and if unoccupied, whether they are suitable to receive translocated ducks. A unique version of the occupancy model is applied to each island in order to predict probabilities of transition between occupancy states given the conditions on that island (e.g., the altitude of habitat areas on the island). Island models will be linked through removals or additions of translocated ducks, and through large-scale events (e.g., a catastrophic storm hitting one island will be more likely to hit nearby islands). The optimization framework allows managers to investigate which combination of translocation actions results in maximum persistence and occupancy across sites.

Lower Flint River basin fishes and drought

To conserve water during critical drought periods, the state of Georgia has established the Flint River Drought Protection Act. The decision about where best to conserve water is complicated by uncertainty about ecosystem responses to changes in stream flows. For an adaptive approach to managing flows in the lower Flint River basin, models were built to evaluate the effects of different water use patterns. Four models incorporated four different hypotheses about the influence of stream flow on the colonization and persistence of fishes. The models represent different biological mechanisms, and they are used to estimate changes in species-specific fish distribution patterns under four simulated water-use scenarios. Learning is facilitated by the comparison of different predictions by the models and the actual fish distribution patterns derived from monitoring data.

Florida scrub-jay habitat

Endemic species like the endangered Florida scrub-jay that depend on a mosaic of scrub habitat have declined significantly as the coastal scrub ecosystem has been changed by fragmentation and fire suppression. Federal and state biologists have begun an adaptive management program to use fire and mechanical means to restore vegetation structure in order to improve the habitat for scrub jays. To represent the potential effects of various management alternatives, habitat models use Markovian transition models to predict rates of vegetation transition between successional stages, while linked occupancy models predict the response of scrub-jays to the vegetation dynamics. These integrated models are optimized to identify the best sequence of management actions to meet objectives related to increasing the viability of the scrubjay population.

Etowah River endangered stream fishes

Urban development north of metropolitan Atlanta threatens endangered stream fishes in the Etowah River. The major aquatic stressor is storm water runoff, with additional impacts from sedimentation, road and utility line crossings, riparian buffer loss, and reservoir impoundments. The Etowah Habitat Conservation Plan, presented to the Fish and Wildlife Service for approval, mandates adaptive management to help local governments deal with urban development while protecting aquatic resources. Occupancy models were constructed to link population indices of three federally listed darters to an indicator of storm water runoff that represents the amount of paved area. Modeling included spatially explicit expressions of probabilities of species occurrence and abundance for different urban development scenarios under the habitat conservation plan. The models are used to predict where the darters are expected to maintain strong populations and where they are expected to decline, for each scenario of future urban growth. Monitoring will provide new observations of species response to development and thus allow the model predictions to be compared with actual data on changes in species occurrence.

Adaptive harvest management

Adaptive harvest management was developed to deal with uncertainties in the regulation of sport waterfowl hunting in North America. Since its inception in 1995, the Adaptive Harvest Management Program has focused principally on the population dynamics and harvest potential of mallards breeding in mid-continental North America. Four alternative population models capture uncertainties regarding the effects of harvest and environmental conditions on mallard abundance. The models result from combining two mortality and two reproductive hypotheses. The mortality hypotheses express alternative views about the effects of harvest on annual survivorship, and the reproductive hypotheses represent alternative views of density-dependent population regulation. Under all four models, reproductive rate is modeled as a function of the number of ponds with water on Canadian prairies in May. Annual changes in pond numbers are represented as a first-order autoregressive process. Different predictions from each of the four models represent uncertainty about population dynamics.

Native prairie restoration in national wildlife refuges

By reintroducing disturbance in native prairies, refuge managers hope to control invasive plants and restore a high proportion of native species in national wildlife refuges invaded by smooth brome and Kentucky bluegrass. Annually collected data on prairie composition allow managers to classify sampling areas into one of 16 categories. Four competing models express different hypotheses about how the individual components of a grassland respond differentially to treatment (e.g., models generally assume that rest is to some degree detrimental; however, one model assumes that the detrimental effect is the same without regard to degree of disturbance in the recent past, whereas another assumes that the effect is less if the prairie has experienced recent disturbance).

5.5. Monitoring Protocols

The importance of monitoring in adaptive management applications is universally recognized, so much so that some people seem to think that monitoring resource conditions is sufficient in and of itself to make a project "adaptive." Monitoring certainly does play a critical role by providing the information needed for both learning and evaluation of management effectiveness. But we emphasize again that, by definition, adaptive management involves not just monitoring, but the implementation and integration of multiple components in assessment and adaptation. The value of monitoring in adaptive management springs from its contribution to decision making, and monitoring protocols should be developed with that in mind.

To make monitoring useful, choices of what ecological attributes to monitor, and how to monitor them (frequency, extent, intensity, etc.), must be linked closely to the management situation that motivates the monitoring in the first place. There are always limits on the staff and funding for monitoring, and it is important to choose design protocols that will provide the most useful information within those limits. Protocol design should be based on the purposes of monitoring and the way in which monitoring data will be analyzed.

Climate change. Monitoring should cover the climate variables that are thought to drive system behaviors, as well as the resource attributes and processes that are affected. Monitoring protocols should specify the attributes to be monitored and methodologies to be used. Because long time periods are often involved, a structured monitoring process might include, for example, frequent monitoring of some biological attributes such as mortality and reproduction rates, less frequent monitoring of landscape attributes such as ecosystem types and locations, and monitoring at decadal or longer intervals for features such as directionality and variation of climate drivers.

Water resources. Monitoring protocols for water resources vary depending on the type of aquatic system and the management objectives. Water flows into and out of a standing water body and water movement in a river or stream can be measured continuously or intermittently. Water quality, temperature, clarity, and concentrations of particulate matter can be measured seasonally or year-round. There are many ways to measure biological components such as aquatic vegetation, fish, and other organisms. Surveys can also be used to track human uses and impacts (recreation, subsistence fishing and hunting, aquaculture).

Energy. For energy development and production, monitoring usually involves the timing, extraction, or amount of energy produced by energy facilities. Often, a utility or corporate sponsor commits to do the monitoring. In many if not most cases, the impacts of energy infrastructure and operations on fish, wildlife, and habitats also need to be monitored.

Human/natural interface. Monitoring protocols for projects in this thematic area target ecological variables and processes that are affected by human disturbance and management actions. Efficiency and accuracy of monitoring-based estimates (of system states, vital rates, or resource aggregates such as biodiversity) are important concerns.

Examples of monitoring protocols

Coastal wetland impoundments and sea level

Many national wildlife refuges maintain coastal wetland impoundments that enhance habitat and attract large numbers of waterbirds and other wildlife, but rising sea levels may eventually lead to removal of some impoundments. To track this threat, monitoring of shorebird and waterfowl numbers, habitat extent and condition (vegetation, water levels), and infrastructure management costs could be conducted annually, with periodic monitoring of sea level. The data from monitoring would be used to determine resource status each year and evaluate progress toward achieving objectives, which might include target numbers of waterfowl to be maintained, as well as specific budgetary limits.

Wyoming Landscape Conservation Initiative

Oil and gas extraction projects on federally managed lands in Wyoming impinge on habitat of imperiled species such as the greater sage grouse, a candidate for listing under the Endangered Species Act. In the Wyoming Landscape Conservation Initiative, management focuses on conserving and enhancing wildlife habitat in areas surrounding oil and gas extraction operations. In the 1990s various vegetation treatments (burns, herbicides) were used to create a mosaic of sagebrush stands in an attempt to provide preferred habitat for sage grouse. Actual use of the treated habitat by sage grouse is monitored by counting foraging pellets and droppings within belt transects on treatment and control sites.

Prairie pothole restoration

The Minnesota Private Lands Program, part of the National Wildlife Refuge System, supports restoration of small privately owned prairie pothole wetlands that were converted to agriculture by draining and filling during the period from the 1950s to the 1980s. Adaptive management of hydrological restoration, sometimes combined with sediment removal, is used to maximize wetland quality for breeding waterfowl. Resource attributes that are monitored include percentage of the pothole filled with water, horizontal interdispersion of vegetation, plant diversity, and invasive species. Monitoring is conducted for 30 minutes per pothole annually for 4 years, and in years 6 and 8 after restoration.

Solar project siting and permitting

In California, proposed industry-grade solar energy projects range in size from 200 to 3,200 hectares. Almost all the land and resources within a project boundary are affected by the placement of solar collectors, service roads, and rainwater retention basins, which can interfere with desert sand transport cycles. In a project sited to reduce blockage of sand moving across the valley, monitoring could be conducted to evaluate whether the infrastructure configuration meets the objectives of maximizing energy production while minimizing impacts on plants dependent on blowing sand. Attributes monitored could include energy production, establishment of blowing-sand-dependent plants downwind, and sand dune stability.

Native prairie restoration in national wildlife refuges

Native prairies in national wildlife refuges of the northern Great Plains are being invaded to varying degrees by plants such as smooth brome and Kentucky bluegrass. By reintroducing disturbance, refuge managers hope to control invasive plants and restore a high proportion of native species. To measure plant community composition, annual belt-transect monitoring on a sample of 25-m transects from each of approximately 120 native prairies provides measures of vegetation composition in four classes: percentage of native grasses and forbs, percentage of smooth brome, percentage of Kentucky bluegrass, and percentage of other plants. These four values are used to assign a particular prairie to one of 16 possible states (for example, one such state is defined as 45to 60-percent native grasses and forbs with the remainder dominated by smooth brome).

River temperature and salmonid survival

Large storage reservoirs behind hydroelectric dams can cause warmer water temperatures, resulting in stress and mortality for salmonid fish and reducing the dissolved oxygen necessary for fish and other aquatic life. Adaptive management to maintain water temperatures and dissolved oxygen at biologically appropriate levels would include monitoring of vertical temperature gradients in the reservoir, water temperatures downstream, and salmonid survival rates. The monitoring data would be used to evaluate effectiveness of management actions (e.g., cold water releases during summer months, reduction of warm water inputs, and water temperature control curtains) and progress toward objectives (e.g., sustaining downstream temperatures below 20°C and increasing salmonid survival).

Adaptive harvest management

Adaptive harvest management was developed to deal with uncertainties in the regulation of sport waterfowl hunting in North America. A major component of the process for setting waterfowl hunting regulations consists of data collected each year on population status, habitat conditions, production, harvest levels, and other attributes of management interest. Waterfowl monitoring in North America is made possible only by the cooperative efforts of the U.S. Fish and Wildlife Service, the Canadian Wildlife Service, state and provincial wildlife agencies, and various research institutions. Among the most important are waterfowl and wetland habitat surveys conducted in the principal breeding range of North American ducks. Waterfowl are also monitored through a large-scale banding program in which individually numbered leg bands are placed on birds, usually just prior to the hunting season. Finally, the Fish and Wildlife Service conducts hunter surveys to determine hunting activity and the size of the waterfowl harvest.

Fire fuel treatments in the Sierra Nevada

Millions of hectares of forest in California are at risk from wildfires. Management of fire fuels on Forest Service lands in the Sierra Nevada has generated controversy for decades. To help reconcile conflicts, an adaptive management project is now being used to implement the 2004 Sierra Nevada Forest Plan Amendment. The project evaluates how different forest vegetation treatments can reduce fire spread and intensity within the constraints of maintaining water quality, residential safety, and wildlife habitat for the Pacific fisher and California spotted owl. The project involves reduction of fire fuels in a series of patches with a method of strategically placed treatments at the landscape level. Fire risk reduction, wildlife impacts, and water quality are monitored at two study areas in 1/20 hectare permanent plots set in a 500-meter grid pattern. Data are collected on forest structure and composition as well as shrubs and fuels. Water quality will be monitored in two sub-watershed areas.

6. Components of the Iterative Phase of Adaptive Management

Adaptive management as we describe it in this guide calls for the elements in Section 5 to be folded into an iterative process of decision making and learning (Figure 2.2). It also is useful to interrupt the technical learning cycle periodically in order to reconsider the set-up elements and incorporate any changes that may be needed if perspectives and values change over the course of the project.

In this section we revisit the processes of the iterative phase of adaptive management – namely, decision making, post-decision monitoring, assessment of monitoring data, learning and feedback, and institutional learning. Again, we use examples from the four thematic areas of climate change, water resources, energy development, and human impacts on the landscape to illustrate the iterative phase. Summaries of the examples are found the appendix.

6.1. Decision Making

We described earlier how adaptive management focuses on management in the face of uncertainty, with the potential to improve management as our understanding of its consequences grows over time. Here we consider the actual process of adaptive decision making, with decisions at each point in time that reflect the current level of understanding and anticipate the future consequences of decisions.

The actual process of adaptive decision making varies depending on the particular project. An institutional framework consists of one or more decision makers along with other stakeholders who provide advice and guidance. Decision making at each decision point considers management objectives, resource status, and knowledge about consequences of potential actions. Decisions are then implemented by means of management actions on the ground.

In some cases the decision process includes only a small number of managers who, for example, adjust water flows or follow mowing schedules on a wildlife refuge. Other decision processes call for a more formal structure of public input, information sharing, and review of proposed actions. For example, a highly structured process is mandated by the National Environmental Policy Act, which calls for engagement of stakeholders and the public, communication of management alternatives, publication of relevant documents, and a final record of decision or other decision documents.

Climate change. Because of the far-reaching impacts of climate change and the broad spectrum of potential stakeholders, decision making for climate change problems will probably involve a rather structured process of stakeholder input that includes federal, state, and perhaps municipal interests. Mitigation actions might focus on regulatory actions, permitting, tax incentives, or policies to reduce greenhouse gas emissions. Adaptation actions might include direct interventions (e.g., species translocation, creation of corridors) as well as regulatory and other policy responses.

Water resources. Water management almost always involves joint consultation and input from stakeholders, often a board of stakeholders with divergent perspectives and values who make recommendations to a water authority. The authority is frequently a government agency such as the Bureau of Reclamation or the Army Corps of Engineers, which presides over the water board. Management actions are often required at regular intervals as determined by seasonal precipitation, snowmelt, and other patterns. Uncertainty about management impacts is addressed by means of experimental interventions (e.g., water releases) that are implemented over time, with follow-up monitoring between interventions to provide new information for future decisions.

Energy. Energy development typically involves federal and state authorization and oversight of permits. Permittees are almost always private energy interests who take on the responsibility for infrastructure development and facility operations. Decision making includes review and approval of proposals for the siting, development, and operation of energy facilities. Decisions about siting new facilities can use information collected at existing facilities, whereas decisions about facility operations can use single-site information collected over time, as well as information collected at other sites.

Human/natural interface. Approaches to decision making in this thematic area vary widely. With some notable exceptions, the elaborateness of the decision making process is linked to the ecological or geographic scale of the problem. For example, annual decision making on a small nature preserve might involve a few resource managers who informally interpret information collected yearly on the preserve and discuss its relationship to the management alternatives. On the other hand, decision making at a regional level would need a more structured and formal process involving federal, state, and non-government interests in joint fact finding and collaborative decision making.

Examples of decision making

Laysan duck translocation and sea level rise

The Laysan duck is an endangered species with only two populations on remote low-lying Pacific atolls. The species' entire range covers less than 9 square kilometers. To increase chances of species survival, Fish and Wildlife Service managers and U.S. Geological Survey scientists are preparing a framework to manage the translocation of ducks adaptively in order to establish other breeding populations in the northwestern Hawaiian islands. Managers will collaborate on operational decisions such as where and when to translocate ducks, contingent upon duck population and habitat status. Quantitative decision analysis with stochastic optimization or simulation methods will support decision making and management.

Glen Canyon hydroelectric dam

The Glen Canyon Dam on the Colorado River was established primarily for water storage and hydroelectric power production, but operations of the dam led to adverse impacts on downstream resources, including endangered native fish downstream in the Grand Canyon. Beginning in 1996, adaptive management principles have been used to help inform changes in dam operations and other activities undertaken to improve resource conditions in downstream areas including Grand Canyon National Park. The adaptive management process works within a legal process on the Colorado River, with changes in dam operations that are designed to improve conditions for endangered species and the downstream ecosystem. Other activities include experimental translocation of endangered fish to other tributaries in order to assess the feasibility of establishing additional breeding populations. The Adaptive Management Work Group, a federal advisory committee, makes recommendations to the Secretary of the Interior on the operations of Glen Canyon Dam.

Cape Cod National Seashore wind turbines

The Cape Cod National Seashore is planning to power some park facilities sustainably with wind turbines to reduce greenhouse gas emissions, within the constraint of conserving park resources (i.e., unacceptable impacts on birds and bats must be avoided). Adaptive management will be used to decide whether and when to adjust or shut down operations of the turbines. The park superintendent will make decisions with input from the Fish and Wildlife Service, the Massachusetts state endangered species program, and the public, contingent on bird and bat mortality resulting from operation of the turbines.

Wyoming Landscape Conservation Initiative

In the Wyoming Landscape Conservation Initiative, adaptive management is used to conserve and enhance wildlife habitat, within the constraint of developing oil and gas resources on predominantly federally managed land. A five-member coordination team is responsible for conservation planning and implementation of adaptive management strategies, and for managing fiscal and logistic operations. Plans for the initiative call for adaptive decision making for habitat conservation and other activities, but not for leasing for energy development.

Adaptive harvest management

Adaptive harvest management was developed to deal with uncertainties about the regulation of sport waterfowl hunting in North America. Early each year, the Fish and Wildlife Service announces its intent to establish waterfowl hunting regulations and provides the schedule of public rule-making. The agency director appoints a Migratory Bird Regulations Committee with representatives of the waterfowl flyway councils, which presides over the process and is responsible for regulatory recommendations. The committee directs a technical working group of biologists to use dynamic optimization to identify optimal regulatory policies that account for breeding population size, environmental conditions, and the current level of understanding. Once the regulations are approved by the director, they provide outside limits (on hunting season length and bag limit) within which the states select their state hunting seasons.

6.2. Follow-up Monitoring

Monitoring, a key component in all applications of adaptive management, provides information to estimate resource status, informs decision making, and facilitates evaluation and learning after decisions are made. In the context of adaptive management, monitoring is an ongoing activity, conducted according to the protocols developed in the set-up phase. In some situations it is undertaken each time a decision is made, for example, when managing species with annual life cycles. In other cases monitoring may be undertaken only after several management interventions, for example, when an ecological system takes a long time to exhibit a response to management.

Project needs determine the timing of monitoring. In many adaptive management applications, monitoring is conducted at fixed and regular intervals. Monitoring can also be applied irregularly, especially if it is tied directly to available funding or if it targets extreme events or unusual disturbances of the resource. In one approach to timing a monitoring effort, monitoring is treated as a part of the decision making process itself, with the decision about whether to monitor at each point in time depending on the status of the resource (estimated from the most recent monitoring effort) and the level of structural uncertainty at that time. For example, a project using this approach might stipulate the monitoring of a population only if its abundance is low and there is a high degree of uncertainty about survival or reproductive potential.

Monitoring can be a highly refined process involving experts and strong controls on field data collection. Alternatively, it can be more loosely structured, perhaps involving a cadre of amateurs who collect the data. In either case, the monitoring program must be carefully designed to ensure a tight connection between management objectives and specific monitoring metrics and protocols so that the data collected are relevant to assessment, learning, and future decision making. Logistical and cost considerations include the time and effort required to get to field sites, the workload per person in the field, the process of recording and verifying field observations, and the amount of training and preparation of people collecting data. Attention to the details of who collects data, and how, are critical to successful resource monitoring.

Climate change. For problems involving climate change, environmental conditions must be tracked by ongoing monitoring in order to determine the direction and variability of environmental change. For monitoring the effects of mitigation and adaptation, variants of a "before versus after and control versus impact" design can help to isolate the effect of an intervention while accounting for changes in environmental conditions. Logistical considerations will depend on the type of problem and interventions. When a project involves monitoring activities across a large area, protocols must be clearly established and personnel must be carefully trained to ensure comparable results.

Water resources. Post-decision monitoring of water resources is usually organized around sequential management interventions and the need to compare their effects over time. Extensive aquatic systems that include both upstream and downstream habitats and conditions present special challenges for collecting and managing data. Water resource monitoring may include acquisition, installation, and maintenance of stream gages and other specialized equipment.

Energy. In many energy projects, private entities take responsibility for collecting and analyzing data as part of the permitting process. Under these circumstances there are requirements from the Data Quality Act for monitoring protocols, quality assurance and quality control, and personnel training. In adaptive management projects there also is an obligation to share data and assessment results among stakeholders so that adaptive adjustments can be made as impacts are recorded. When data are collected from different sites, standards need to be in place for consistency and comparability.

Human/natural interface. Monitoring activities under this theme are based on the type of project. All the logistical and operational issues mentioned in the introduction to this section may be relevant. Special concerns are the accessibility of sampling locations and the detectability of organisms at sample sites. Flexibility is needed in order to adjust monitoring protocols when some field locations become inaccessible. Because fish and other wildlife can be difficult to observe in natural settings, a statistical treatment of detectability should be incorporated into protocol designs when monitoring these resources. People who collect data may need to be trained in field procedures (e.g., how to estimate distance or wind speed; how to identify bird songs).

Examples of follow-up monitoring

New England shrub habitats on national wildlife refuges

Shrub communities on wildlife refuges in the northeast support migrating land birds and the New England cottontail rabbit, a candidate for listing under the Endangered Species Act. Fish and Wildlife Service managers are using adaptive management to control the invasive plants that degrade native shrub communities and reduce the food resources required by rabbits and birds. Refuge biologists train seasonal field staff and supervise a monitoring effort that targets a number of metrics related to plant and wildlife composition and abundance. Pellets are collected for cottontail surveys by a two-person team three times each winter, and mapping-grade GPS units are used to relocate points each year. Bird surveys are conducted during the fall migration (September – October) over 8 to 10 person-days for each refuge, and vegetation surveys including berry counts are conducted over 12 to 14 person-days. Stem counts are made after leaves drop, and can take a week for a team of four biologists. Each type of monitoring has a time window that allows for variable weather conditions.

Adaptive harvest management

Adaptive harvest management was developed to deal explicitly with multiple sources of uncertainty in the regulation of sport waterfowl hunting in North America. Each spring, duck abundance and habitat conditions are monitored in over 5 million square kilometers of breeding habitat, with 89,000 kilometers of aerial transects. Ground surveys are conducted on a subset of the aerial transects to estimate the proportion of birds that are undetected from the air. The central portion of the breeding range is surveyed again in mid-summer to estimate the number of duck broods, and to assess the progress of the breeding season. These surveys have been operational since the 1950s, and they provide critical information for setting annual duck-hunting regulations. Federal and state biologists who are carefully trained in species identification and field techniques participate in these surveys.

Waterfowl are also monitored through a large-scale banding program in which individually numbered leg bands are placed on over 350,000 birds annually, usually just before the hunting season. A waterfowl harvest survey is conducted each year via a mail questionnaire, which is completed by a sample of 30,000 to 35,000 waterfowl hunters across the United States. In addition to the questionnaire, about 8,000 hunters send in wings or tails of harvested birds so that the species and demographic structure of the harvest can be determined.

6.3. Assessment

In an adaptive management project, the data produced by monitoring are used along with other information to evaluate management effectiveness, understand resource status, and reduce uncertainty about management effects. Learning is promoted by comparing predictions generated by the models with data-based estimates of actual responses. The similarity between predicted and observed responses is used to judge model adequacy and thereby improve understanding. Monitoring data can also be compared with desired outcomes in order to evaluate the effectiveness of management and measure its success in attaining management objectives. In addition, monitoring data are used to estimate particular resource attributes and compare projected costs, benefits, and impacts of management alternatives for future decision making.

It is not uncommon for the assessment component of adaptive decision making to be underemphasized or under-resourced, especially if adaptive management is viewed simply as sequential decision making interspersed with monitoring. A common, though unjustified, assumption is that the monitoring data "speak for themselves" and require little if any analysis. In contrast, we emphasize how important it is to analyze monitoring data in learning-based management. But the staff time and other resources needed for this task should not be underestimated.

Climate change. Assessment in climate change includes evaluation of resource responses to mitigation and adaptation actions, by comparing predicted responses with observations from monitoring. Because climate may change unpredictably, it is important to include an analysis of the potential for changing patterns in environmental conditions. This might involve different climate models or scenarios, with analysis of management strategies to determine which can best meet objectives in the face of uncertainty about future climate conditions. Dealing with potentially unstable climate and resource conditions, and the uncertainties associated with them, presents a serious challenge.

Water resources. Because water systems are fundamentally dynamic and influenced by environmental conditions and management actions, an adaptive management framework of sequential decision making and learning applies naturally to many water projects. Assessment can often be fairly straightforward, with an evaluation of water interventions, analysis of potential outcomes of management options, and comparison of predicted and observed patterns of change in water conditions.

Energy. Assessment of energy projects focuses on the analysis of data on the impacts of siting, infrastructure, and operations of energy facilities. Assessments might include estimating parameters such as mortality, reproduction, and migration rates of animals and plants affected by energy development. Other assessments could involve a comparison of resource conditions before and after energy development, by investigating attributes such as the distribution and abundance of species or the fragmentation and disturbance of landscapes.

Human/natural interface. Assessments for this broad class of problems can include a great many analyses, such as comparing effects of different management actions on resources, or evaluating the effectiveness of different strategies in achieving objectives. Assessment may also focus on learning, as in the comparison of predicted responses to management and actual responses recorded by field monitoring. Analyses may focus on the statistical association of resource and socio-economic data.

Examples of assessment

New England shrub habitats on refuges

Shrub communities on wildlife refuges in the northeast support migrating land birds and the New England cottontail rabbit, a candidate for listing under the Endangered Species Act. Fish and Wildlife Service managers are using adaptive management to control the invasive plants that degrade native shrub habitats. Assessments focus on restoration objectives, and monitoring data are used to track progress toward objectives (control of invasive plants and restoration of shrub community integrity), to determine the current status of the shrub communities and fauna of interest, and to make comparisons with predictions of the models aligned with low-and medium-intensity treatments. The comparison between observed and predicted metrics allows for updated measures of confidence in the two kinds of treatment used to restore the shrub community.

Prairie pothole restoration

The Minnesota Private Lands Program (part of the National Wildlife Refuge System) and other federal partners support restoration of privately owned small prairie pothole wetlands that were converted to agriculture. Adaptive management is being used for hydrological restoration, sometimes combined with sediment removal. Evaluation focuses on the effectiveness of the management alternatives (hydrology restoration alone versus in combination with sediment dredging) in maximizing wetland quality. Technical analyses include assessment of expected changes in metrics for each of the alternative treatments, and updates of confidence weights for the competing models by comparing predicted versus observed pothole changes.

Vernal pools and amphibians

Landscape changes have degraded ephemeral vernal pools in the eastern United States. Potential impacts due to climate change could further stress vernal pools, specifically by altering hydroperiod length and water depth. This could lead to the decline of many amphibians, such as wood frogs, that depend on vernal pools for breeding. Management of vernal pools may become necessary to ensure adequate habitat for breeding frogs, especially near the southern edge of the range where multiple years of reproductive failure have produced documented declines. Biologists are evaluating whether direct manipulation of pool structure and water retention (e.g., by use of impermeable liners) can increase amphibian colonization and breeding success. Annual monitoring of egg masses, late-stage tadpoles (an indicator of successful breeding) and breeding adults allows biologists to identify ponds for direct manipulation. Field data are also used for comparisons with the predicted responses to management and anticipated climate patterns.

Florida scrub-jay habitat

The Florida coastal scrub ecosystem is highly modified by fragmentation and fire suppression, which has resulted in significant decline of endemic species like the endangered Florida scrub-jay. To measure progress toward restoration of a mosaic of successional stages following fire and mechanical treatments, managers annually monitor vegetation structure from aerial photographs and conduct presence/absence surveys for scrub-jays. Data collected at the patch level are used to describe current resource status. By comparing actual status with the status predicted by linked habitat transition–occupancy models, managers are able to learn how fire or mechanical treatments affect vegetation transition rates, and thereby reduce a key uncertainty in managing for improved habitat for scrub-jays.

Adaptive harvest management

Adaptive harvest management was developed to deal with uncertainties in the regulation of sport waterfowl hunting. Each year assessments incorporating different models of waterfowl populations and management alternatives are used to support decision making, evaluation, and learning. Regulatory decisions are based on comparisons among potential outcomes of different actions. Learning is promoted by comparing predictions from each of four population models with waterfowl population estimates derived from monitoring. Comparing outcomes with population objectives is used to evaluate how well harvest objectives are being met.

6.4. Learning and Feedback

In adaptive management, the understanding gained from monitoring and assessment helps in selecting future management actions. It is the iterative cycle of decision making, monitoring, and assessment that leads gradually to better understanding of resource dynamics. As understanding evolves, so should decision making.

Several approaches to learning can be used; all involve using monitoring data to update confidence in the models under consideration. The enhanced understanding then guides decision making at the next time period. One common approach involves updating the measures of confidence associated with different models by combining them with current monitoring data via Bayes' rule to produce new confidence measures for the next time (Lee 1989).

One can think of the iterative learning cycle as starting with a management decision, followed by post-decision monitoring and the subsequent assessment of monitoring data, with feedback of what is learned into future decision making (Figure 2.3). Alternatively, one can think of the process as beginning with monitoring, followed by analysis of the resulting data, followed by decision making based on what is learned. In either case the sequence of activities is repeated over the course of a project, during which learning occurs and management strategy is adjusted accordingly.

Climate change. Climate change will create new challenges to learning, arising from the instability that climate change induces in patterns of resource change. The environmental variations defining climate change can influence the uncertainty factors in adaptive management (see Section 4) and produce deep uncertainties about resource dynamics and decision making. When the resource system itself is changing over time, learning-based decision making becomes especially difficult. One way to approach the problem is to use scenarios of different environmental futures, and learn about their relative adequacy by means of monitoring resource attributes and environmental conditions.

Water resources. Learning in water resource projects centers on structural uncertainty about hydrological processes and rates. Hydrological models that express structural uncertainty describe different trajectories for water conditions, flows, aquatic organisms, etc, which can be compared with actual states estimated from hydrological and other monitoring. Learning can be pursued with classical experiments according to a management design, or with sequential updating of model confidence using Bayes' rule.

Energy. Learning and feedback in energy projects relates to the impacts of siting, infrastructure development, and operation of energy facilities. At specific sites, project evaluation is often based on monitoring data used in Bayesian updating of model weights, resulting in better understanding that can be applied to future management decisions about operations. In larger-scale evaluations, information and understanding from one site can be applied to other sites to guide development as they are being established. In either case, what is learned is folded into future decision making.

Human/natural interface. Learning in this context is often based on interventions replicated over time rather than space, because many projects involve animals or plants in the wild and occur at scales that don't allow replication in space. That said, some problems are more amenable to spatial rather than temporal replication, for example, large-scale management of old-growth forests in which responses to management interventions occur after long time lags. In both instances the data produced by monitoring can be used to assess the system responses to management over time, with new understanding used to adjust management.

Examples of learning and feedback

New England shrub habitats on refuges

Shrub communities on wildlife refuges in the northeast support migrating land birds and the New England cottontail rabbit, a candidate for listing under the Endangered Species Act. Fish and Wildlife Service managers use adaptive management to control the invasive plants that degrade native shrub communities. Learning is promoted by updating credibility weights of two competing models of low-and medium-intensity treatments of invasive plants on the basis of monitoring data. The two models differ in how much effort is needed to restore native shrub communities successfully. The data also can be used to refine the models and improve parameter estimates. What is learned in the project will be relevant to the choice of treatments for shrub habitat management in other coastal areas in New England.

Native prairie restoration in national wildlife refuges

Native prairies in national wildlife refuges of the northern Great Plains are being invaded by plants such as smooth brome and Kentucky bluegrass as a result of the suppression of natural disturbance. Managers choose annually among alternative treatments to restore a high proportion of native species. Environmental variability across spatial and temporal scales compounds the inherent difficulty of choosing the best management action to reach established restoration targets. Uncertainty is represented by a set of four competing models that express alternative hypotheses about vegetation responses to management. The annual cycle involves treatment, monitoring, and assessment of data against model-based predictions of prairie responses. The credibility weights of the models are revised annually with monitoring data and used to identify an optimal action for the following year. Information on vegetation response and actions implemented is added to a permanent database that can be used for evaluation and periodic revision of the predictive models.

Adaptive harvest management

Adaptive harvest management was developed to deal with uncertainties in the regulation of sport waterfowl hunting in North America. Each year, a proposed policy for waterfowl hunting regulations is derived by dynamic optimization methods. After regulatory decisions based on this policy are made, model-specific predictions for subsequent breeding population size are compared with monitoring data as they become available, to produce new model credibility weights with Bayes' rule. The process is adaptive in the sense that the harvest policy "evolves" over time to account for new knowledge generated by the comparison of predicted and observed population sizes. The change in harvest policy from 1995 to 2007, resulting from changing model weights, is a striking example of the efficacy of adaptive management as it is actually implemented.

Great Barrier Reef marine reserve management

The Great Barrier Reef is a 2,000-kilometer-long complex of coral reefs and other ecosystems such as coastal seagrass beds and diverse sea-floor habitats covering 135,000 square kilometers off the northeast coast of Australia. It is a national marine park that contains the world's largest network of marine reserves, which are designed systematically at a regional scale. Adaptive management is used to restore ecosystem structure (e.g., widespread recovery of depleted fish stocks) and to prevent ongoing degradation (e.g., reduced coral mortality). The Great Barrier Reef Zoning Plan 2004 protects living marine resources including apex predators (reef sharks) and commercially fished reef species (coral trout, redthroat emperor) with different levels of zoning. Monitoring is used to evaluate effectiveness of management strategies in meeting objectives (e.g., by comparing conditions before and after zoning implementation, or replicates across a range of zones or other gradients), as well as effectiveness of enforcement. For the objective of restoring ecosystem structure, monitoring of juvenile and adult fish to estimate species population demographics has shown significantly greater reproductive output and transport of larvae of coral trout and redthroat emperors from no-take zones compared with fished zones, thus indicating that the no-take network provided ecosystem-wide population increases for recovery of fish stocks. Surveys of reef sharks showed higher abundances in no-entry zones than in no-take zones, which suggested possible compliance problems requiring further management action in no-take zones. For the objective of preventing degradation, monitoring of crown-of-thorns starfish (the major historical cause of coral mortality) and coral cover has shown strong positive connections among no-take reserve zones, reduced starfish outbreaks, and reduced coral mortality, thus indicating that zoning benefits the entire reef ecosystem.

6.5. Institutional Learning

Periodically we may need to interrupt the technical cycle of decision making, monitoring, assessment and feedback, in order to reconsider project objectives, management alternatives, and other elements of the set-up phase. This reconsideration constitutes an institutional learning cycle that complements, but differs from, the cycle of technical learning. In combination, the two cycles are referred to as "double-loop" learning. By recognizing uncertainty about the architecture of decision making and allowing for reduction of that uncertainty over time, the institutional learning cycle expands the possibilities for learning in adaptive management. Important considerations are the frequency of revisitation of the set-up elements, which elements to revisit, how to recognize the need for adjustments, and the type of adjustments to be made.

In practice, the cycle of technical learning occurs more rapidly than that of institutional learning, with the institutional cycle producing less frequent changes of the set-up elements. Changes of objectives, management alternatives, and other elements that are too frequent can compromise both institutional and technical learning, by confounding their effects (Williams 2010*a*).

In many adaptive management projects, both kinds of learning are important. It is sometimes as useful to understand and track evolving social and institutional relations and stakeholder perspectives as it is to resolve technical issues about resource structure and process (Williams 2006). Although adaptive management can improve resource management by reducing structural uncertainty, the improvement can be stalled if social and institutional changes, which are inevitable over time, are not taken into account. Because early successes in achieving objectives can result in social and institutional changes, it is important to acknowledge and if possible account for them as decision making progresses.

Climate change. The uncertainties associated with climate change, in which directional changes in environmental conditions induce unstable (non-stationary) resource dynamics, are sure to offer many opportunities for double-loop learning. As the direction and magnitude of environmental change are revealed by monitoring environmental conditions, adjustments are likely to be needed in the models, alternatives, and even objectives, so that the decision making elements can be "recalibrated" to the patterns of systemic change.

Water resources. The multiplicity of values and perspectives that enter into adaptive decision making about water resources heightens the potential for change in the set-up elements. In particular, the pressure to change objectives can increase as monitoring data begin to reveal unexpected patterns in resource responses to water management. For example, a dam project that is managed for irrigation and power generation might reveal steadily declining native fish populations that require additional modeling and assessment. More generally, the potential for building up disproportionate benefits or costs among stakeholders can lead to revision of the management objectives for a project, or at least changes in weighting their relative importance. This in turn can lead to revising alternatives, monitoring protocols, or other elements.

Energy. Double-loop learning can play an important role in renewable and non-renewable energy projects. For example, decisions about the siting of facilities might meet initial objectives but nevertheless lead to an acknowledged need to consider other factors in decision making. Likewise, it may become clear over time that key aspects of facilities support and operations were not included in initial planning, or important stakeholders were not included, or stated objectives weren't adequate for evaluation and decision making. Under these circumstances the decision making apparatus of adaptive management can be revised by changing the set-up elements.

Human/natural interface. Adaptive management projects in this field often need to change project objectives and projection models. As evidence of resource responses to management accumulates, stakeholders may revisit objectives and other elements in an effort to make strategies more responsive to their needs. As mentioned above, it is important not to change the set-up elements too frequently because rapid change can interfere with the rate of both technical and institutional learning.

Examples of institutional learning

Blanca wetlands

The Blanca Wildlife Habitat Area in southern Colorado is an area of over 6,200 hectares of marshes, ponds, and periodically flooded basins called playas, which provide habitat for a wide variety of wildlife and plant species. The 1995 management plan for this area focused on a core area of 1,100 hectares for which the Bureau of Land Management has adequate artesian water. Since then, Bureau managers have learned that playa basins should be flooded only once every 3 to 6 years in order to produce the very high densities of the insects and vegetation critical for wetland birds. After revisiting the management alternatives, managers now are attempting to mimic the historic hydrology of playas by drying larger areas rather than individual basins. This involves rotation of the limited artesian water around an expanded area over multiple years, so that the longer drying times correspond to the natural hydrology of playas. Revised objectives place more emphasis on supporting shorebird populations because, as other wetlands in the region have been lost, Blanca has become the most important shorebird area in the San Luis Valley.

Northwest Forest Plan

The 1994 Northwest Forest Plan for federal lands in the range of the northern spotted owl formally established a regional effectiveness monitoring program with a feedback process using a 10-year interpretive report. The final report included a synthesis of new science and results from five monitoring modules, with direct participation by top interagency decision makers. An important lesson learned was that the belief held by most people that monitoring results would be clear and easily applicable in future decision making is incorrect, at least with raw data. The findings suggest that monitoring data can be used more effectively in an adaptive learning cycle when they are given a management context and assessed through structured interactions between researchers and decision makers. Recognition of the importance of assessment and an increased emphasis on it has led to changes in the framing of adaptive forest planning and management.

Adaptive harvest management

Adaptive harvest management was developed to deal with uncertainties in the regulation of sport waterfowl hunting in North America. Perhaps one of its greatest contributions is a capacity for managers to re-examine their purposes and rules of operation. The periodic examination of adaptive management components has usually been precipitated by an institutional recognition that current elements and protocols are inadequate to address unanticipated problems arising in management policy. For example, difficulties have arisen in recent years in defining unambiguous harvest objectives, in predicting and regulating harvests, and in coping with the tradeoffs inherent in managing multiple stocks of waterfowl exposed to a common harvest. The key challenge facing harvest management is whether the decision making structure of adaptive harvest management can itself be adaptive, that is, whether the knowledge and experience gained in its application can be reflected in higher-level structural adjustments when needed. Sorting out these policy and institutional issues will require innovative mechanisms for producing effective dialogue and new ways of handling disputes within a process that all parties regard as fair.

Columbia River chinook salmon

Dams that have been established on the Columbia River for hydropower, irrigation, and flood control have adversely affected spawning and recruitment of fall-run chinook salmon. Public utility districts of the middle Columbia River work with federal and state agencies and Native American tribes to set priorities for power generation and fish and wildlife protection. Dam relicensing by the Federal Energy Regulatory Commission highlighted the need to protect chinook spawning areas in the Hanford Reach of the Columbia. An adaptive management working group representing the stakeholders therefore established a procedure for water releases to minimize the risk that breeding areas would dry out from water fluctuations in the river, within the constraint of meeting energy demands. After implementation of the initial hydropower plan, follow-up monitoring revealed that once chinook fry emerged from the breeding areas, they remained in the natal areas and did not move as those areas dried out under a post-breeding flow regime. This left juveniles stranded and perishing in large numbers, and threatened the gains realized by protecting spawning grounds in the fall. The working group established flow bands that took into account the volume of water being released from Grand Coulee Dam upstream, and suggested limits on the range of possible flows. This expanded the water release agreement to cover a longer time period from spawning through rearing. By altering the management options on the basis of monitoring in the Hanford Reach, the working group used double-loop learning to accelerate progress in achieving the objective of increasing chinook reproductive success.

7. Integrating the Components of Adaptive Management

In previous sections we discussed the elements and processes of adaptive management as we define them in this guide, and illustrated them with examples from the thematic areas of climate change, water resources, energy development, and human impacts on the natural landscape. We treated the components of adaptive management separately in individual section sections in order to highlight the common features of each component among the themes.

In this section we show how these components are integrated in the application of adaptive management in the field. Our examples include management of river flows, management of breeding habitat of an endangered woodpecker species, management of food resources of migratory shorebirds, and management of disturbance near nesting eagles. Each example is comprehensive, in that it includes all the interacting components of adaptive management. In the interest of brevity we omit many of the details required to develop the application fully, and limit ourselves to the information needed to describe the actual implementation of adaptive management.

7.1. Tallapoosa River – R.L. Harris Dam in Alabama

Extensive hydropower development has altered riverine habitats in the southeastern United States, which is a global center of freshwater fish and invertebrate diversity. The Tallapoosa River in east central Alabama is a priority area for aquatic conservation, with a native fish assemblage of 57 species, including 5 species endemic to its river system. Four of the fishes and one mussel are considered to be "at risk" by the Fish and Wildlife Service. Fish and invertebrate populations in one of the highest-quality segments of Tallapoosa habitat were threatened with destruction by daily extreme low flows that dried the river bed, extreme flow variation from floods to trickles, and daily temperature changes from pulsed water releases for hydropower at the utility-owned R.L. Harris Dam.

The Fish and Wildlife Service has been evaluating proposals for relicensing of more than 200 dams in the southeastern United States – including the Harris dam – that are licensed by the Federal Energy Regulatory Commission. Through the Southern Rivers Integrated Science Initiative, the Service has recognized the need for new approaches to evaluate dam relicensing, and new strategies to mitigate the impacts of dam operations on aquatic communities. Rather than the one-time fixed flow regime typical of relicensing prescriptions, adaptive management has been used on the Tallapoosa since 2005 to allow for the adjustment of flow management based on what is learned from system responses. This project is intended to provide a template for incorporating adaptive management and decision support into the relicensing process.

Set-up phase for the Tallapoosa River project

Stakeholders. Project leaders took steps early on to involve stakeholders actively. Neutral, professional third-party facilitators were engaged to help develop and conduct stakeholder fora and workshops, and to gather information from stakeholder polls. Stakeholders created a governance structure, the R.L. Harris Stakeholder Board, for future decision making . The board includes representatives from the Fish and Wildlife Service and other federal agencies, state and local agencies, conservation groups, river-boating and sport-fishing groups, property-owner groups, and the utility company that owns the dam. Special care was taken to be as inclusive as possible so that all groups and individuals with an investment in the system could have a part in management discussions. Equity in stakeholder representation was sought, in order to avoid skewed voting from overrepresentation of one entity or viewpoint.

Objectives. Through the facilitated workshops, stakeholders arrived at 10 fundamental objectives that they agreed were representative of all involved parties. Many objectives were in conflict, with potential conflicts centering around maximizing hydropower production and reservoir levels versus maximizing aquatic biodiversity and downstream boating opportunities. The competing stakeholder objectives were incorporated in a decision support framework, with software that created visual representations of the influence diagram of relationships among objectives, as well as visualization of the Bayes belief network and the decision support model. Tradeoffs among all the objectives were considered in developing decision support procedures in which all stakeholders "give a little" to negotiate a starting point for management actions.

Management alternatives. To compromise among user groups, management decisions focused on three main decisions: daily flow rates, seasonal flows for boating, and fish spawning windows (periods of stable flow for spawning). A stream gage in an unregulated stretch of the Tallapoosa provided control data on natural stream flows. Management alternatives were developed for each of the three main decision points, i.e., four alternative daily flow patterns, four alternative spawning window options, and two boating flow options. For example, the primary decision concerned daily flow operations from the dam. The four alternatives to the primary decision were: (*i*) current utility operation, with no change from the twice-daily peak flow pulses of 4 to 6 hours, followed by almost no flow; (*ii*) constant minimum flow to maintain the "natural" target as recorded by the stream gage, plus necessary power generation flows; (*iii*) constant flow to maintain the "natural" target, but never falling below 300 cubic feet per second, plus necessary power generation flows; (*iv*) twice-daily flow pulses to maintain at least 75 percent of the "natural" target (an option proposed by the utility company).

Models. Hypothesized relations between flow features and system responses were modeled by means of a probabilistic Bayes' network. Modeling incorporated four alternative primary flow regimes based on different a priori hypotheses about how fishes and habitat would respond to specific flow conditions. Modeling also included four alternative options for spawning windows – periods of stable flow that allow fish to spawn and juveniles to develop successfully – that expressed different hypotheses about how recruitment of juvenile fish of different species would respond to seasonal spawning windows in spring and summer. Optimization was used to determine the management decision that maximized stakeholder values, which included improving fish habitat and recruitment of juveniles, improving downstream boating during peak season, and maintaining sufficient flow levels for power generation.

Monitoring protocols. Uncertainty about functional relations among flow parameters (e.g., frequency, duration, magnitude) and fish populations needs to be resolved, especially the relations between periods of stable flow and recruitment of young fishes. Protocols were developed for fish sampling as well as the measurement of water flows (e.g., river stage, water column velocity, and substratum type at sampling sites). Data collection was designed to evaluate effects of various flow regimes on occupancy, availability, and persistence of the shallow-slow and shallow-fast habitats needed by various species for spring and summer spawning and survival of young of the year.

Iterative phase for the Tallapoosa River project

Decision making. Decision making incorporated the 10 fundamental objectives that were developed by stakeholders, plus the three main decisions (daily flow pattern, stable flows for fish spawning, and flows for boating). Stakeholders negotiated the starting point for management actions – an initial flow prescription that consisted of (*i*) pulsed flows to increase base flow from the dam, thus mimicking natural hydrology in an unregulated reach of the Tallapoosa; (*ii*) periods of stable flows for fish spawning in both spring and summer; and (*iii*) suitable flows for downstream boating in October.

Post-decision monitoring. Faunal response to management is monitored by collecting numerous fish samples from sites below the dam and in nearby unregulated river reaches. Fish occupancy, extinction, and colonization probabilities are estimated at least twice a year at multiple, randomly selected sampling sites, with pre-positioned area electrofishers (electrodes powered by generators) to stun fish so they can be netted and identified, counted, and measured. Population parameters are being modeled as a function of habitat variables, site location (regulated or unregulated), and attributes related to water availability in the basin and management at the dam. River hydrology data are measured by U.S. Geological Survey flow gages. Stakeholders are involved in aspects of planning and execution of the monitoring plan.

Assessment. Monitoring data collected since 2005 are being used to modify biological hypotheses. Data on flows, habitat characteristics, and fish populations are being analyzed for comparison with predicted responses of fish and habitats to management actions. The decision model was based on hypothesized relations between flow features and fish population responses: depleted low flows, flow instability, and thermal-regime alteration were the main factors hypothesized to affect fishes. Ten explicitly stated uncertainty nodes (e.g., reservoir inflow, lake levels, shallow-fast habitat, slow-cover habitat, degree days, small fish abundance, bass recruitment, redbreast sunfish spawning success) are parameters linked directly to fundamental objectives of stakeholders and hypotheses related to system function. The new information about actual system states will reduce uncertainty about the relationships between flow and system responses.

Learning and feedback. The models are used to predict outcomes of future flow manipulations, which then are compared with actual flows to facilitate learning. Data collected in post-decision monitoring are used in updating the probabilities that represent uncertainty about fish distributions, hydrological flows, and recreation capacity. As uncertainties about the relationships between flow and system responses are reduced, managers and stakeholders will be able to adjust the flow regime as needed to meet management objectives and ensure conservation of at-risk species.

Institutional learning. The original design for monitoring has been adjusted to account for detectability of organisms through the use of occupancy sampling and estimation. An upcoming review of the decision making process will consider possible changes in other elements of the adaptive management apparatus, including objectives and management alternatives. For example, modification of the underlying biological hypotheses may lead to revision of the models in which they are embedded. If all objectives are attained, future flow adjustments may become necessary to mitigate the effects of other watershed changes that affect flow regimes. Such changes could include drought, land-use changes that affect runoff, or climate change.

7.2. Red Knots and Horseshoe Crabs in Delaware Bay

The sandy beaches of Delaware Bay in Delaware and New Jersey are globally important as spawning grounds for Atlantic horseshoe crabs and as stopover habitat for long-distance migratory shorebirds such as the red knot. Each year the birds stop in Delaware Bay in May to rest and replenish their energy reserves during migration from wintering grounds in temperate and tropical regions to breeding grounds in the Arctic. In the bay, they feed on the seasonally superabundant horseshoe crab eggs deposited on the beaches by millions of crabs that spawn during the lunar tides each spring. Throughout the 1990s a growing and unregulated harvest of horseshoe crabs, for use as bait in eel and whelk fisheries, led to a decline in spawning crabs.

In the late 1990s and early 2000s, monitoring data began to show major declines in red knot abundance. Shorebird scientists and advocacy groups identified horseshoe crab fishing as the root cause of the red knot decline, and claimed that reduced horseshoe crab egg abundance resulted in decreased survival and reproductive success of migrating birds. Other scientists and horseshoe crab fishermen's groups argued that red knots are not solely reliant on horseshoe crab eggs for food, and that some other environmental factor must be responsible for red knot declines. Conservationists called for a complete cessation of horseshoe crab fishing in the Delaware Bay, while others called for more moderate regulations in order to protect the horseshoe crab fishery. Highly variable data, which could be interpreted to support either side in this ongoing argument, resulted in substantial scientific and decision making uncertainty. Adaptive management was initiated on this contentious issue, with a goal of identifying a sustainable horseshoe crab harvest strategy that protects red knots and enables learning about how the system functions.

Set-up phase for the red knot and horseshoe crab project

Stakeholders. The horseshoe crab harvest and red knot conservation problem involves numerous stakeholders. The crabs are commercially harvested for bait in eel and whelk fisheries, and are vital to the biomedical industry that uses their unique copper-based blood for medical testing. The red knot is a candidate species for listing under the federal Endangered Species Act and is listed as endangered or as a species of conservation concern in several states. The adaptive management effort has engaged the Atlantic States Marine

Fisheries Commission; the Fish and Wildlife Service; the New Jersey, Delaware, Maryland, and Virginia state fisheries and wildlife agencies; the New Jersey Audubon Society; and the Conserve Wildlife Foundation of New Jersey, among other stakeholder organizations. Representatives from the organizations collectively make up a stakeholder committee.

Objectives. Working with the stakeholder organizations, the Delaware Bay adaptive management team (composed of scientists and experts from the various organizations and the U.S. Geological Survey) has developed a unified objective statement that effectively captures the competing resource uses. After extensive discussions, the stakeholders agreed on the statement, "Manage harvest of horseshoe crabs in the Delaware Bay to maximize harvest but also to maintain ecosystem integrity and provide adequate stopover habitat for migrating shorebirds." In order to introduce quantitative, measureable attributes for monitoring purposes, this statement was effectively translated as, "Maximize horseshoe crab harvest as long as red knot population abundance has exceeded some predetermined threshold (45,000 individuals)." The latter objective uses an increase in red knot populations from their current population size of about 20,000 to 45,000 as a surrogate measure for ecosystem integrity and adequate stopover habitat. The red knot abundance metric met the true fundamental objective of several stakeholders, which was to restore red knot populations to some higher level of abundance.

Management alternatives. Because the decision maker and sponsor of the framework development is the Atlantic States Marine Fisheries Commission, management alternatives were restricted exclusively to crab harvest actions. The stakeholder committee considered historic harvests, fishing industry needs, and conservation community concerns in developing a range of harvest actions that reflect those needs and concerns. The possible actions ranged from a full moratorium, to the harvest of as many as half a million crabs, and allowed for differential harvest actions for male and female crabs.

Models. The modeling portion of the Delaware Bay adaptive management project focused on three primary hypotheses about the ecological interactions between the two species. (*i*) The first hypothesis was that horseshoe crab spawning abundance (the number of crabs that crawl up the beach to spawn in the spring) has *dramatic effects* on red knot annual survival and reproductive success. Essentially, birds that do not gain enough weight (i.e., cannot find enough food) during stopover have high mortality and those that do manage to survive the rest of migration that year do not breed. (*ii*) The second hypothesis was that horseshoe crab spawning abundance has a *small effect* on red knot survival and large effect on reproductive success. In the model for this hypothesis, birds that do not gain enough weight during stopover survive the rest of the year with no residual effect, but do not attempt to breed. (*iii*) The third hypothesis was that horseshoe crab populations have *no effect* on red knot population dynamics. This hypothesis assumes that some other environmental issue caused the decline in the red knot population, if in fact the decline truly happened (observed declines may simply be a result of changes in habitat use, or alterations of migratory patterns, or systematic changes in detection rate). These different models predict very different responses by the red knot population to horseshoe crab harvest actions.

Monitoring. Annual decision making requires estimates of the abundance of horseshoe crabs and red knots. The population of adult horseshoe crabs is surveyed annually with a stratified-transect sampling design during the late summer and fall, after the crabs have spawned and returned to deep waters. Offshore trawling is used to dredge up sampled crabs. In past years, red knot abundance was estimated from aerial survey counts conducted in the

Delaware Bay during the stopover season. The peak count for a season was considered an index of abundance; however, aerial counts are subject to tremendous counting error and other statistical issues. The adaptive management team recommended abundance estimates based on mark–recapture techniques, which will make use of the mark and recapture effort carried out annually in the bay to assess red knot weight and body condition.

Iterative phase for the red knot and horseshoe crab project

Decision making. In its current form the adaptive management plan calls for annual decisions about harvest regulations. Managers need to assess the abundance of both horseshoe crabs and red knots to determine the best management action, given the state of the two populations and the recognized ecological and environmental uncertainty. Adaptive stochastic dynamic programming techniques provide decision makers with a decision table of optimal harvest actions based on different possible states of the system and the current degree of understanding about the system. The decision recommendations seek to maximize harvest yields over a long time horizon while protecting red knot populations.

Post-decision monitoring. The harvest action is implemented in the summer and fall, after red knot spring migration and crab spawning. The timeline for decision making, assessment, and monitoring is complex, because the action implementation is concurrent with or even later than the assessment monitoring for the next year's decision. The effects of the harvest may not be apparent in assessment and monitoring data for 2 or more years. Following a harvest decision and implementation, managers need to estimate abundance in the same way used to assess the populations before the decision implementation.

Assessment. The three alternative system models corresponding to the three alternative hypotheses make different predictions about red knot abundance in response to horseshoe crab harvest actions. Comparing observed or estimated red knot abundance to the three model predictions allows managers and researchers to determine which of the three hypotheses more effectively represents red knot responses to horseshoe crab harvests.

Learning and feedback. By applying management actions and comparing the observed results with predicted outcomes from the three models, one can gradually learn which model more accurately predicts the system response to horseshoe crab harvest. Confidence will accumulate over time in the model that makes the best predictions about red knot populations. At the beginning of the process, model confidence values are established through expert opinion and stakeholder input. As decision making progresses over time, the model confidence values will be updated using Bayes' rule. The process of sequential assessment and model updating will gradually increase knowledge about the relationship between red knots and horseshoe crabs.

Institutional learning. Every few years, the set-up phase of the adaptive management plan will be revisited. Stakeholder groups will reconvene, objectives will be re-evaluated, and the models (and underlying hypotheses) will be re-evaluated in accordance with what was learned in the iterative phase. As an additional component of the set-up phase, the adaptive management framework for this problem identifies research priorities to address some uncertainties that could not be incorporated into the initial set of three models. Some issues like sex ratio linkage to fertility in horseshoe crab populations, juvenile survival rates of red knots, and first-year survival rates of horseshoe crabs were put aside during the set-up phase, with the intention of revisiting them as new data become available, or as other studies produce results that can be incorporated to improve model predictions. There was disagreement and uncertainty among stakeholders and scientists as to which issues were central to the key ecological relationships; the choice of the particular issues underlying the current set of models represents a compromise on the important hypotheses about ecological relationships. The remaining issues and disagreement were set aside to prevent excessive complexity from inhibiting management decision making. Meanwhile, plans were put in place to address those issues in parallel with iterative decision making, as part of the double-loop learning process.

7.3. Southeastern Pine Forests and Red-Cockaded Woodpeckers

The endangered red-cockaded woodpecker occurs in mature pine forests of the southeastern United States, most typically in longleaf pine forests of the coastal plain. Patches of old-growth forest provide critical nesting habitat for cooperatively breeding woodpeckers; family groups include helpers at the nest and may be as large as nine birds. Preferred sites are mature, park-like pine stands about 4 hectares in area. The birds select old trees for the excavation of nesting cavities, and family units defend territories around clusters of such trees. Other habitat requirements include over-story and mid-story layers of limited density and an adequate understory, but the old-growth condition is the underlying requirement for successful breeding by woodpecker groups. These habitat conditions were routinely met by the historic disturbances that shaped southeastern pine forests. Red-cockaded woodpeckers also occurred in other pine forest types and in provinces beyond the coastal plain, including loblolly pine forests of the Piedmont.

The recovery plan for the species calls for establishment of primary and secondary populations across different forest types and provinces. One recovery target is the Piedmont National Wildlife Refuge and Chattahoochee–Oconee National Forest complex in central Georgia. These lands came into federal ownership in the 1930s after the collapse of cotton farming in the region. Since then, forests of mixed loblolly pine and hardwoods have become established. The red-cockaded woodpecker population in this forest complex is the largest in the Piedmont physiographic province. Creation and long-term maintenance of old-growth forest is critical for sustaining this population.

The recovery plan for red-cockaded woodpeckers provides guidance to forest managers on the amount and age-class distribution of annual cutting necessary to sustain old-growth conditions. But these guidelines were derived mostly from experience with longleaf pine forests in the coastal plain, and they do not take into account the current composition of a mixed loblolly pine–hardwood forest or the rate of succession from pine to hardwood in the Piedmont. A faster rate of succession to hardwoods would limit the ability to create old-growth loblolly pine forest, and management strategies would vary depending on this rate. Unfortunately the rate of succession is unknown, so the maximum amount of attainable old-growth forest and the best sequence of harvest actions to reach it are also unknown. At the Piedmont refuge, adaptive management can account for this biological uncertainty in guiding decisions about the harvest strategy to maximize old-growth loblolly pine habitat over the long term.

Set-up phase for the pine forest and woodpecker project

Stakeholder involvement. Final decisions about forest management rest with the refuge manager. However, decisions are made with an awareness of legal mandates as well as the views and demands of different stakeholders. The refuge manager is obligated to meet legal requirements imposed by the Endangered Species Act and to act in accordance with the recovery plan for red-cockaded woodpeckers. Unfortunately, actions under the recovery plan guidelines potentially run counter to management needs of other trust species, which are also obligatory. The manager must be sensitive to needs of the public for consumptive use of the refuge lands and recreational access to them. Finally, the manager must try to provide positive benefit to adjacent landowners and the local community, or at least avoid antagonizing them. Thus, the refuge manager makes each decision in a context of conflicting desires and expectations among stakeholders.

Management objectives. One of the fundamental objectives of management at the Piedmont refuge is to establish a self-sustaining red-cockaded woodpecker population. In the mixed forest settings typified at the refuge, it is clear that achievement of this goal requires active forest management to maintain old-growth forest habitats. Therefore, creation of old-growth habitat was seen as a necessary means to achieve the fundamental objective. Because "sustainability" is a key attribute, an objective for habitat management was defined with a long time horizon. The management objective for the project was the accumulation of the largest sum of annual amounts (hectares) of old-growth pine forest (80 years and older) over a very long time (1,000 years).

Management alternatives. Annual forest harvest and regeneration activities are the means by which managers pursue a future stream of old-growth forest habitat. The refuge's forest managers take these actions for broad age classes of the forest. Pine stands in the refuge are classified into one of four age groups: P1 (age 0 to 16 years), P2 (age 16 to 40 years), P3 (age 40 to 80 years), and P4 ("old-growth" forest, age 80+ years). Managers contract with private operators to harvest trees in the three older groups (P2 to P4) that produce merchantable timber. Therefore, management alternatives each year are the total amounts of timber harvest from each of the classes P2 through P4. This decision applies to the total annual amounts of harvest, but the specific stands from which timber is cut are determined according to a compartment rotational schedule.

Models. The total forest area of the Piedmont refuge is portrayed at any time as a distribution among five distinct forest types: the four pine classes P1 to P4, and an upland hardwood class, UH. The distribution of these types changes from year to year as a result of transitions among the classes, which are influenced by factors that managers control (harvest) and factors that they do not. Harvest moves portions of classes P2 through P4 into class P1. Growth advances portions of younger pine classes into older classes. Random disturbances such as wind, storms, or insect infestations cause portions of the age classes to transition to P1. Annual forest succession results in transition to type UH by portions of all pine types. Parameters that describe these transitions either exist or can be reasonably inferred, except those for hardwood succession. The limited data that exist provide a wide range of plausible rates of succession. To account for this uncertainty, three models were constructed with different rates of hardwood succession. Given a current forest state (the distribution of

Piedmont refuge forest among forest types) and a management action (amount of harvest from each class, P2 through P4), each model generates a distinct prediction of forest state in the next year. The models have different implications about the maximum amount of old-growth pine forest that can be sustained through harvest, as well as the means by which to achieve that outcome.

Monitoring protocols. The annual sampling plan includes basal area, over-story density, stand type, and stand age. These data provide a means of measuring forest composition for decision making and assessment of the predictive quality of the models. However, the annual surveys are conducted on only one of eight subsets of the refuge's 34 management compartments each year. A survey of the entire refuge therefore is accomplished every 8 years. At longer but irregular intervals, a complete forest assessment is available through interpretation of remotely sensed data. To integrate the time step of monitoring (8+ years) fully with the time step of model prediction and decision making, either of two approaches can be used. One is to conduct an annual forest-wide survey for the key variables of interest, perhaps at reduced spatial density and in conjunction with some other type of resource monitoring (e.g., bird counts). Another option is to recast the decision framework in a time step that more closely matches the temporal resolution of the available data. For example, recasting the problem in an 8-year time step would produce an 8-year schedule of actions (but also an 8-year time interval between learning opportunities).

Iterative phase for the pine forest and woodpecker project

Decision making. With knowledge of the current composition of the refuge forest and uncertainty about the rates of hardwood succession, forest managers reach a decision each year about the total amount to cut out of the P2, P3, and P4 pine forest classes to sustain a maximum amount of old-growth forest. Optimal decision analysis with adaptive stochastic dynamic programming accounts for the current forest composition, degree of uncertainty about hardwood succession, and future forest dynamics resulting from a current harvest decision. A critical feature of the decision analysis is that it explicitly includes the possibility of learning to help resolve uncertainty and improve long-term management. In effect, "experimental" actions, which involve some near-term resource sacrifice but have the potential for longer-term resource gain, are to be compared with actions that preserve short-term gain but offer little expectation of learning.

Post-decision monitoring. Refuge biologists conduct a systematic (grid-based) sampling of the forests each year over a subset of the 34 management areas that constitute the refuge. The current scheme of rotational timber surveys results in opportunities for model assessment only every 8 years, whereas changes in forest states are perceptible over much shorter time periods. An alternative that includes annual assessment of refuge-wide forest state (with lower spatial density of sampling points and collection of the most critical variables for decision making) would provide the information for incremental updates of knowledge about forest dynamics before each decision.

Assessment. Each of the three alternative models generates a distinct prediction of the forest state following a harvest decision. Forest monitoring data that are collected before the next action provide a means of assessing how well the models perform. For example, the amount of P4 forest occurring at the next time period is one of the state components predicted by each model. Because the models contain random mechanisms (to mimic random disturbances and other random transitions), each model predicts a distribution of P4 forest amounts rather than a single value. These distributions are compared with the monitoring data characterizing the amount of forest-wide P4.

Learning and feedback. At each time step in the decision making process, the three models are evaluated with monitoring data and the outcomes are accumulated in model credibility weights. If a model's prediction agrees well with the data, its credibility increases. If a model's prediction agrees poorly, its credibility declines. The updating of weights is accomplished through application of Bayes' rule each year. Because credibility is gained by some models and lost by others, uncertainty about hardwood succession is successively reduced, and the quality of future decision making improves. After the learning and feedback step, the adaptive management cycle is completed when the forest manager uses the new information about model credibility in making decisions.

Institutional learning. A closer integration of the current monitoring program with the decision structure would permit a more informed implementation of an adaptive framework for forest decision making on the Piedmont refuge. At some time after implementation, there may be a need to review and revise elements of the process. For example, the management objective currently has no component that reflects the cost of producing P4 habitat. A cost component could be incorporated, which could include real financial costs of carrying out the harvest actions or the ecological costs borne by other species in the conversion of suitable forest habitat to unsuitable early succession habitat. Another example would be the possibility of learning over time that hardwood succession is so rapid that it makes the creation of any meaningful amount of old-growth habitat an unreasonable prospect. Such a finding could stimulate a search for new management alternatives, such as the installation of artificial cavities in younger stands that are less vulnerable to hardwood succession.

7.4. Golden Eagles in Denali National Park

Throughout the Northern Hemisphere, the golden eagle is the pre-eminent diurnal predator of medium-sized birds and mammals in open country. The mountainous regions of Alaska's Denali National Park support the highest nesting density of golden eagles in North America, with abundant snowshoe hares, ptarmigan, and other prey and undisturbed cliffs for nests that are used over decades or even centuries. Nesting eagles are sensitive to human disturbance, and the National Park Service must limit human presence near nest sites in order to maintain Denali's eagle population. During their reproductive cycle of nest repair, egg-laying, and brood rearing, eagles may occupy any of nearly 100 potential nesting sites across the northeastern part of the park between March and September. Denali is also a premier destination for wilderness recreation during the summer months, during which back-country hiking, airplane tours, and other recreational activities may negatively affect the occupancy of potential nesting sites by eagles and therefore reduce overall breeding success. In 2007, National Park Service biologists and managers at Denali began collaboration with U.S. Geological Survey scientists to develop an adaptive management project to manage human disturbance of nesting golden eagles.

Set-up phase for the golden eagle project

Stakeholder involvement. Stakeholders for this project consist of a small group of federal agency managers and scientists. National Park Service managers include the inventory and monitoring coordinator for the Central Alaska Network and the biologist responsible for the annual eagle monitoring program. Collaborators from the U.S. Geological Survey include an Alaska Science Center scientist familiar with the eagles and with adaptive management, and two scientists from Patuxent Wildlife Research Center with expertise in animal monitoring methods and decision analysis. The superintendent of Denali National Park is the ultimate decision maker for any Denali management efforts.

Management objectives. Objectives for national parks usually include conservation of natural areas and ecological systems, as well as facilitation of human enjoyment and use. Park managers are aware that these two basic objectives may be in conflict. The general objectives of Denali's adaptive management project are to maintain eagle numbers at historical levels while permitting recreational use of the Park. The adaptive management working group specified a desired threshold number of golden eagle nesting territories at which successful breeding occurs. The primary management action for Denali managers is the closure of potential nesting sites to recreational hikers. Thus, the specific objective was to maximize the number of potential nesting sites that are open to hikers, subject to the constraint that the projected number of successful breeding sites the next season exceeds the established threshold.

Management alternatives. Adaptive management focuses on hiker disturbance. Of all potential nest sites, only those near the main road through Denali were thought to be exposed to hiker disturbance. The potential management actions thus involved closure of as many as all of these sites, or closure of as few as none. The specific management decision was how many of these sites to close to hiking next season, on the basis of information obtained about eagle occupancy and reproductive success during the current breeding season.

Models. The previous monitoring efforts provided a useful data set for an analysis in which occupancy estimation models accounting for detectability were fitted to historical monitoring data. These analyses suggested that the proportion of eagle nest sites at which successful reproduction occurs is affected by both human disturbance and snowshoe hare (prey) abundance. These relationships were incorporated into one model of eagle occupancy and reproductive success. However, the evidence in favor of this model was not overwhelming, and there was substantial uncertainty about factors influencing eagle occupancy and reproductive success. This uncertainty was expressed by the development of two additional models. One depicted virtually no effect of disturbance on eagle reproductive success, whereas the other reflected a strong effect. The data-based model was intermediate between these extreme models in terms of human disturbance effects. Reduction of this uncertainty (i.e., settling on a single most plausible model) is expected to lead to improved management.

Monitoring protocols. The replicated surveys of all potential nesting sites each breeding season provide the information needed to estimate the proportion of sites occupied by eagles and the proportion of sites at which successful reproduction occurs. Data on hare abundance collected during these surveys provide an index of hare abundance. These quantities then become the predictors of subsequent eagle occupancy and reproductive success in all three management models.

Iterative phase for the golden eagle project

Decision making. Objectives, actions, models, and current understanding were used with dynamic optimization to produce optimal decision matrices. To use these matrices the manager simply needs to specify the current condition of the system (eagle occupancy and reproductive success, hare abundance) on the basis of the most recent monitoring results. An optimal management action is then identified for each of the possible estimates of eagle and hare "state."

Post-decision monitoring. The current monitoring program will continue throughout the adaptive management project. All potential nest sites are visited by helicopter and on foot in the spring and summer. For inference about occupancy, sites are visited on multiple occasions until eagles are detected, with a maximum of three visits per site. Each site at which eagles are detected is visited again in July to assess reproductive success. Data (fecal pellet counts) for a hare abundance index are collected at each site as well.

Assessment. Each of the three alternative models generates a distinct prediction about the proportion of sites that are expected to be occupied by eagles the next season and the fraction of those at which reproduction is successful. The predictions are not single values but distributions of values, reflecting the uncertainty of any predictive process. These predictions are then used in the subsequent learning phase.

Learning and feedback. Comparisons of the model-based predictions with the monitoring estimates of eagle occupancy and reproductive success provide information about the predictive abilities of each model, with changes in the measures based on a comparison with monitoring estimates. Specifically, the adaptive management process includes measures of relative credibility for each model. The changes in credibility measures effectively modify the influence of each model in the decision process so that models that are better predictors gain more influence. Changes in these measures provide a quantitative measure of learning.

Institutional learning. A monitoring program for golden eagles has been ongoing for over two decades, and the current management program provides an explicit process for using monitoring information directly to make management decisions. After some experience with this program, a logical next step would be to consider other potential sources of disturbance such as airplane flights for tourists. Future management actions in this case would entail specification of flight paths that limit potential disturbance to eagle nest sites. Another extension might be to incorporate annual estimates of the annual numbers of visitors at the sites.

8. FUTURE DIRECTIONS

The Department of the Interior and other natural resource organizations must grapple with critical decisions affecting our nation's resources and environment. These decisions bear directly on management of our lands and waters, the development of renewable and nonrenewable energy, and our responses to climate change and the continuing alteration of nature by human activities. It will be increasingly important to make resource decisions in a structured and transparent way that is based on science and accounts for uncertainty. Because adaptive management meets these conditions, it can be a valuable template for effective decision making by managers in the DOI bureaus.

In this guide we have described the components of adaptive management as interconnected and mutually reinforcing. We've argued that models and management alternatives need to be developed synergistically and framed in terms of learning and management objectives. A critical assumption underlying the adaptive management framework is that science activities (modeling, decision analysis, assessment, learning/feedback) are embedded in a context of natural resource management, where learning is valued because it contributes to management.

Adaptive Management and Planning

We have characterized adaptive management in this guide in terms of a set-up or deliberative phase in which the elements of adaptive decision making are developed and refined, and an iterative phase in which those elements are incorporated into an ongoing cycle of decision making, monitoring, assessment, and learning (Figure 2.2). However, adaptive decision making also can be usefully portrayed in terms of planning and learning. For example, the adaptive learning cycle is often described as a cycle of planning, implementation, tracking, and feedback (U.S. Fish and Wildlife Service 2006; Figure 8.1).

There are natural linkages between these two perspectives. For example, one can recognize the essential elements of strategic planning (the setting of objectives, selection of alternatives, prediction of consequences, metrics for tracking results, etc.) in our set-up phase. On the other hand, the elements of strategy implementation, such as monitoring, feedback, and adjustment, are represented in our iterative phase. Finally, the larger adaptive cycle of institutional learning and adaptation is expressed through double-loop learning. In this sense, adaptive decision making can be seen as an ongoing cycle of planning, implementation, and learning.

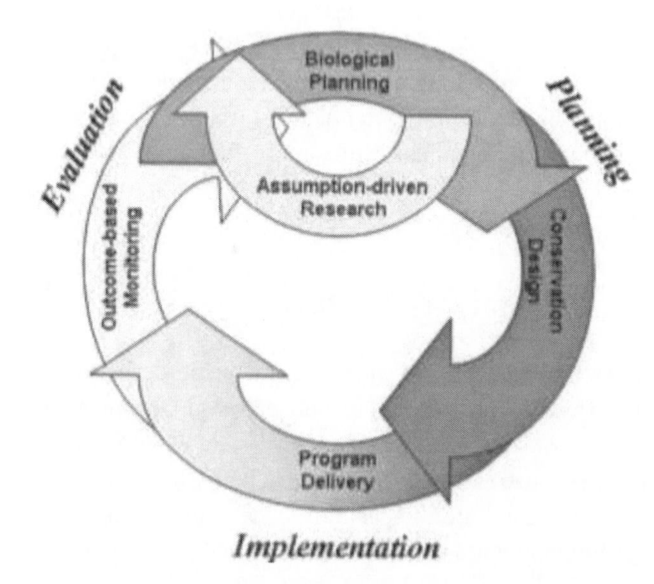

Figure 8.1. The adaptive cycle in terms of planning, implementation, and evaluation and learning.

All government agencies are currently engaged in both strategic planning and the tracking of results in plan implementation. Thus, their business practices already involve many of the important elements of adaptive management. A remaining need is to incorporate learning as a fundamental element of strategic planning and implementation, whereby the learning resulting from monitoring and assessment is fed back into future planning. By proactively linking plan implementation to plan development through a learning process, the adaptive cycle of learning-based management is completed and becomes standard business practice. A number of important questions need to be addressed in completing the cycle – for example, how to recognize and represent uncertainty, how to track it over time, and how to reduce it efficiently through learning-based management. Nevertheless, the practices currently used for natural resources management in DOI have the potential to be incorporated naturally into an adaptive approach.

Stakeholder compromise

Active stakeholder engagement helps parties learn from each other, find areas of common ground, and build trust in developing management strategies collaboratively. Among other things, collaboration reinforces the sharing of viewpoints and objectives, and promotes efforts to find acceptable management options among stakeholders. When effectively managed, active stakeholder engagement can help to avoid the paralysis that otherwise can be induced by uncertainty (or disagreement) about management impacts and the controversy that uncertainty brings.

However, the challenges in managing stakeholder involvement should not be underestimated. Strong disagreements among stakeholders about management objectives, alternatives, and consequences are common in natural resource management. Without a process for revisiting these elements as management proceeds over time, stakeholder commitments to decision making by consensus can easily collapse into confrontation and even litigation. It is much easier to agree to move forward with a management strategy if everyone understands that objectives, management alternatives, and the other elements of decision making can be reviewed and renegotiated as new evidence about management performance becomes available. Such an arrangement offers an incentive to stakeholders to agree on an initial strategy that involves compromise on all sides. On the other hand, negotiation to establish a fixed and inflexible strategy leaves all parties with less flexibility as they hold out for their ideal conditions because they think the outcome can't be changed.

The point here is that a possibility of learning from system performance, and then adjusting management strategy based on what is learned, can foster collaboration and aid decision making. In that sense, the expression and treatment of uncertainty, which is one of the key challenges in adaptive decision making, is also one of its strengths.

Synthesis of advances in adaptive management

Two broad focus groups have worked more or less in parallel but independently to develop adaptive management of natural resources. One group focuses on technical issues (models, metrics and propagation of uncertainty, projection of the future consequences of present actions, optimal decision making in the face of uncertainty). This guide provides a framework for incorporating these issues into the process of adaptive decision making. The other group focuses on collaboration (institutions, stakeholders, cooperative interactions, elicitation of stakeholder values and perspectives). Throughout this guide we have pointed out the latter issues, and in particular the role of stakeholders in all aspects of adaptive decision making. The many examples we include here all emphasize the importance of incorporating stakeholder values when identifying objectives, acceptable management alternatives, and models that express stakeholders' perspectives.

At present, the collaborative and technical thrusts in adaptive management are being pursued separately. For the most part, researchers, practitioners, and even organizations tend to emphasize either one thrust or the other. The challenge is ultimately to join the two in a more unified vision and process in which each reinforces and strengthens the other. We hope this guide will promote that integration.

Applications of adaptive management in the thematic areas

Although we have emphasized four thematic areas that are important to DOI, the practice of adaptive management is not developed evenly in these areas. For example, there are many examples in the area of human/ natural interactions, and few in climate change. In part this is because the roots of adaptive management are in renewable natural resources, especially biological resources. Applications of adaptive decision making have been documented for many different biological problems, such as fish and wildlife harvest, insect pest control, endangered species recovery, invasive species control, and wetland management. The examples of adaptive decision making in biology are extensive and varied, as one might expect of applications developed over the course of more than 40 years.

Conversely, climate change has only recently become a principal focus of conservationists and managers, and is yet to mature as a field of investigation with an agreed-upon conceptual and methodological framework. Under these circumstances it is reasonable to expect fewer examples of adaptive decision making for climate change mitigation and adaptation. But opportunities for adaptive decision making are likely to grow rapidly, because systemic environmental change, whether a manifestation of long-term climate patterns or the result of human-induced landscape alterations, almost certainly will continue well into the future. Environmental change will continue to produce highly uncertain changes in natural resource systems, and resource managers will have to learn about these systems as they are changing. In this guide we have suggested some ways of framing this problem in terms of adaptive management, but much more work needs to be done. As the urgency of coping with long-term environmental change increases, there is little doubt that the breadth of adaptive management applications will increase as well.

Adaptive management and ecosystem services

Like all strategic approaches to the management of natural resources, adaptive decision making can have unintended consequences, often for resources that aren't the target of the application. Such impacts are often inadequately monitored. The developing field of ecosystem services can contribute to a framework for evaluating management impacts on the quantity and value of services provided by ecosystem attributes and processes. Its integration into adaptive management can be seen most clearly in the production and valuation of ecosystem services, the integration of these values into objectives, and the prediction of changes in ecosystem services and their valuation with models. The connections between adaptive management and ecosystem services need further research, but there are obvious opportunities for collaboration between these important fields of investigation.

Adaptive management and sustainability

Throughout this guide we have emphasized the importance of accounting for the future consequences of present actions. The idea of change over time is fundamental to adaptive management, whether in terms of changing environmental conditions, repeated adjustment of management strategies, or the use of dynamic models that characterize resource changes. By its very nature, adaptive management requires us to sustain resource structures and functions in order to sustain the ecosystem values that contribute to long-term objectives. In particular, adaptive decision making has to be flexible and resilient enough to respond to the inevitable surprises that arise in resource management; only then can ecosystems and their values be dependably maintained in the future. Resilience, vulnerability, and risk all have important roles in adaptive decision making, and their linkages need further examination and development.

As we have described it in this guide, adaptive management can be applicable to local resource projects as well as large-scale conservation programs, though the operational and legal constraints on an adaptive approach may differ across scales. But the basic framework presented in the guide, involving an iterative process of management, monitoring, and evaluation, applies in either case. The key issues in deciding to use adaptive management are whether there is substantial uncertainty about the impacts on management, and whether the reduction of that uncertainty can be expected to improve management.

The framework for adaptive management presented here is not conceptually complex. However, adaptive decision making does require users to acknowledge and account for uncertainty, and maintain an operating environment that allows uncertainty to be reduced through careful planning, evaluation, and learning. An initial investment of time and effort by stakeholders and implementing organizations will increase the likelihood of better decision making and resource stewardship in the future. In addition, the parties must commit to providing the necessary resources for monitoring and assessment over a project time frame to make progress in achieving project objectives. The associated up-front costs are compensated by more informative and collaborative resource management over the long term.

Adaptive management holds great promise in expressing and reducing the uncertainties that keep us from managing natural resources effectively. In many cases, the use of management itself in an experimental context may be the only feasible way to gain the understanding needed to improve management. Producing better understanding by means of transparent, objective driven decision making is one important way to promote the conservation of America's natural resources for future generations.

Appendix. Overviews of Selected Examples

Native Prairie Restoration on the Northern Great Plains

Less than 3 percent of the original vast landscape of native prairies survives across the northern Great Plains. Invasive plant species compound the threats to remnant prairies from habitat fragmentation and development. Prairie grasses and wildflowers such as sideoats grama, big bluestem, prairie blazingstar, and ox-eye sunflower are being overgrown by invasions of cool-season exotic grasses like smooth brome and Kentucky bluegrass, mainly because of the elimination of fire. The restoration of native plant composition in tall-grass and mixed-grass prairies helps to reverse environmental damage, improve water quality, preserve animal habitats, and support species diversity. On national wildlife refuges in the northern Great Plains states, fire and other disturbances such as grazing and haying have been suppressed for decades. By reintroducing disturbance, refuge managers hope to control invasive plants and restore a high proportion of native species. Given the current state of a particular refuge, managers face annual decisions about whether to burn, graze, or hay at all – and if so, which option, and in what manner of application. The biology of the system is poorly understood, as are the effects of treatments, particularly over the long time frames relevant to restoration. Therefore, refuge managers use adaptive management to overcome uncertainty about the best treatment to apply at each point in time to reach the long-term objective of high native composition at least cost.

Endangered Mussel Translocation

Almost one-third of the world's freshwater mussel species occur in the continental United States, which has the world's most diverse mussel fauna. Yet in the last 100 years, no other wide-ranging group has suffered a greater decline. Mussels are filter feeders that are important conduits of the energy fixed by phytoplankton photosynthesis to other parts of the food web. They filter contaminants, sediments, and nutrients from the water column, and hence are sensitive to siltation, pollution, agricultural runoff, impoundments, and invasive species. Their presence (or absence) is a good indicator of water quality and the integrity of ecological processes in a watershed. Northern riffleshell mussels have disappeared from their former range in the Ohio and Maumee River drainages to such a degree that they are now endangered. When bridge construction on the Allegheny River resulted in a formal Endangered Species Act consultation with the Fish and Wildlife Service, a mussel relocation program was mandated. Almost 1,800 riffleshells from the Allegheny were translocated to eight sites in a 2-mile reach of the Big Darby Creek, Ohio, where a small remnant population still existed within the species' historic range. Translocation will continue to be an important recovery strategy, and adaptive management will be used to apply information about the conditions most conducive to survival and reproductive success of the Big Darby mussels to future mussel restoration efforts.

Wyoming Landscape Conservation Initiative

Wyoming's Green River basin contains some of the nation's best sagebrush, mountain shrub, aspen, and riverine habitats. These habitats are crucial for deer, elk, bighorn sheep, pronghorn antelope, and threatened sagebrush-dependent species such as the greater sage grouse and pygmy rabbit. Almost three-quarters of the basin's 6 million hectares are public lands; the remaining lands consist of family farms and ranches. Abundant reserves of minerals and natural gas, oil, coal, and wind make the area a hotspot of industrial energy development. The Bureau of Land Management manages federal land and grants leases for energy development. The Wyoming Landscape Conservation Initiative was launched in 2007 to conserve and enhance wildlife habitat as much as possible in areas of oil, gas, and other resource development. It is a consortium of federal, state, and local agencies; environmental and recreation groups; industry; and private landowners. As energy operations continue, adaptive management will be used to share information among stakeholders, prioritize habitat enhancement projects, and advocate best practices in reclamation and mitigation of industrial development.

New England Shrub Habitats for Rabbits and Migratory Birds

Profound alterations in land use have resulted in loss of early successional forest habitats characterized by thickets of native shrubs in the northeastern United States. The introduction of aggressive exotic invasive species such as the multiflora rose, glossy buckthorn, and honeysuckles, which choke native shrubs, has changed the vegetative composition of the thicket habitats available to species that depend on these habitats. The New England cottontail rabbit and Neotropical migrant birds like warblers and vireos have declined along with native shrub communities. The New England cottontail is a candidate for federal listing under the Endangered Species Act and requires shrub habitats with a high stem density. Fall-migrating land birds rest and feed in thicket habitats, gaining energy from fruits of several native shrub species. Managers of National Wildlife Refuges want to restore biological integrity and diversity of shrub habitats sufficient to support migrant land birds and a sustainable population of New England cottontail rabbits. Vegetation treatment options include lowand medium-intensity treatments that incorporate a combination of mechanical and chemical means to control invasive species, and methods to propagate native shrubs. Adaptive management will be used to determine how much effort is needed to restore native shrub communities at the lowest cost.

Etowah River Endangered Stream Fishes

The southern Appalachian highlands are a global hotspot of fish endemism. The Etowah River in northwestern Georgia supports four endemic fishes, as well as another eight species endemic to the greater Mobile River basin. These and other aquatic species are at risk from urban development and population growth in the Atlanta metropolitan area. The major aquatic stressor is storm-water runoff, in addition to sedimentation, road and utility line crossings, riparian buffer loss, and reservoir impoundments. Three Etowah endemic fishes, darters in the perch family, are already federally listed under the Endangered Species Act. The Act prohibits actions that result in harm to listed species or their habitats, unless explicitly permitted. Adaptive management connects to Endangered Species Act processes by means of the Habitat Conservation Plan (HCP). The Etowah HCP, presented to the Fish and Wildlife Service for approval, incorporates concrete policies (such as runoff limits) for reducing the impacts of urbanization on the endangered darters. It uses models to predict species abundance given HCP implementation, and requires monitoring to provide new information on fishes' responses to development. If actual responses differ from those predicted, the HCP will allow adjustment of urban development policies.

Blanca Wetlands

For thousands of years, the lakes, marshes, and shallow playa basins of the San Luis Valley in southern Colorado filled with snow-melt runoff in late spring and were dry by late summer. By 1950, the basins had dried up entirely due to drainage, wetland loss, and diversion of traditional source waters. In 1965, the Bureau of Land Management began a series of wildlife habitat projects to restore some of the San Luis Valley's dry playa basins to their historic wetland characteristics. Today, the Blanca wetlands site is intensively managed for waterbird, waterfowl, and shorebird habitat. It encompasses over 6,200 hectares of low dunes and depressions that are seasonally flooded by artesian water or canals. As water flows by gravity through the reserve, ponds, marshes, subsaline wetlands, and hypersaline playas are produced sequentially, resulting in a diverse mosaic of wetland habitats. Blanca is one of Colorado's most significant wetland areas, with breeding populations of the white-faced ibis and western snowy plover as well as native amphibians. Adaptive management is used to manage local water flows in order to produce the salinity levels and seasonal vegetation needed by particular species groups.

Cape Cod National Seashore Wind Turbines

The seas off Cape Cod, a peninsula that extends nearly 100 kilometers into the Atlantic Ocean off the coast of Massachusetts, have been called an ocean graveyard. Legendary marine storms have resulted in a rich maritime history. Over 3,000 shipwrecks occurred on the Cape over the past 300 years, with an average of 2 wrecks every month during the winters of the early 1800s. Lighthouses lit by whale-oil lamps, and an efficient lifesaving service put in place by the national government in 1872, helped to reduce the number of shipwreck casualties. Today, the National Park Service manages many unique historic structures and cultural resources associated with the Cape's maritime past, as well as its marine and terrestrial ecosystems, protected in nearly18,000 hectares of the Cape Cod National Seashore. The winds that once drove ships into treacherous shoals will be used to run wind turbines at two locations in the park. The National Park Service's Climate Friendly Parks program aims to power park facilities sustainably, with reduced greenhouse gas emissions. Adaptive management will be used to adjust turbine operations daily or seasonally in order to minimize collisions with bats and birds, which themselves are important park resources.

Prairie Pothole Restoration

When the glaciers of the last ice age receded from the upper Midwest, they left behind millions of shallow depressions – prairie potholes – that fill with snow-melt and rain in the spring. The prairie pothole region is the heart of what was once the world's largest grassland. Millions of ducks and geese pass through this region each spring to nest in the grasslands. It is also important migration habitat for waterfowl breeding in the northern boreal forests and the Arctic. In addition to providing habitat for waterfowl and many other animal species, the pothole wetlands control floods, filter out sediments and contaminants, and recharge groundwater. From the 1950s to the 1980s, thousands of these small wetlands in North and

South Dakota and parts of Nebraska, Minnesota, and Iowa were drained, filled, and converted to agriculture. Now, the Minnesota Private Lands Program, part of the National Wildlife Refuge System, the U.S. Department of Agriculture's Natural Resources Conservation Service, and the Minnesota Department of Natural Resources are collaborating with private landowners to restore prairie pothole wetlands in Minnesota. Their objective is to restore healthy, functioning wetlands across the landscape for waterfowl and migratory bird breeding habitat. Removing the extra sediment from the historic basin as part of the restoration process may expose the native seed bank, thus supporting native wetland revegetation. The primary uncertainty is whether or not sediment excavation, in addition to the usual practice of restoring hydrology, will lead to a higher-quality wetland restoration than simply restoring hydrology. Adaptive management is being used to determine if the benefit of sediment removal justifies the additional cost.

Las Cienegas

A small part of the area that was once the 400,000-hectare Empire Ranch in southeast Arizona contains some of the rarest habitat types in the Southwest. The cienegas (marshlands), riparian cottonwood–willow forests, sacaton grasslands, mesquite bosques, and semi-desert grasslands are part of 18,000 hectares of grassland and oak savanna woodland, the Las Cienegas National Conservation Area, watered by the perennial stream of the Cienega Creek. The area, now part of the Bureau of Land Management's National Landscape Conservation System, was acquired by the Bureau in 1988 and was designated a national conservation area in 2000. It supports six endangered species and many other special status species, such as the threatened Chiricahua leopard frog. The historic Empire Ranch house has been preserved; cattle-grazing operations continue under a Bureau of Land Management lease within the conservation area. Because the area is only an hour from Tucson, development threatens these protected lands with overuse of water, introduction of exotic invasive plant and animal species, and other problems. Adaptive management is used to manage vegetation treatments for grassland restoration in upland areas, and to manage aquatic habitats for federally listed species.

Columbia River chinook salmon

For hundreds of miles upstream, the rivers of the Northwest once boiled with millions of chinook and other salmon migrating from the Pacific Ocean to spawn in the streams of their birth. After years at sea, each fish finds its way home to its own natal stream. By the 1890s, dams were affecting salmon runs. Hydroelectric, flood-control, and irrigation projects eventually reduced the area available to salmon by half and led to precipitous declines. Today, out of approximately 1,000 native migratory salmon stocks on the West Coast, 106 are extinct and 314 are at risk of extinction. In the Columbia River, there are three major races of chinook, which enter the river in spring, summer, or fall runs. The races also vary in the age and timing of descent to the sea by the finger-sized juveniles. The Columbia's fall chinook stock is one of the more productive naturally reproducing stocks in a river system where many salmonids are declining. River flows modified by upstream hydropower dams have been found to be a major factor affecting fall chinook production. Inadequate water supply and extreme fluctuations in water releases have caused spawning grounds to dry out, thus killing eggs and young fish. In a complex regulatory milieu involving federally and privately owned dams, federal and state agencies, and Indian nations, conditions for dam relicensing by the Federal Energy Regulatory Commission resulted in a program of specific water releases to help limit the risk that fish will spawn in areas that dry out. Within the constraint of maintaining hydropower supply, adaptive management is being used to manipulate flows to protect spawning grounds and thus enhance fall chinook reproduction and recruitment in the Hanford Reach of the Columbia.

Florida Scrub-Jay Habitat

The endemic Florida scrub-jay is designated as threatened under the Endangered Species Act. Scrub-jays are restricted to Florida scrub, a rare habitat characterized by evergreen, xeromorphic shrubs including oaks, repent palms, and ericaceous shrubs. Scrub is maintained by frequent fires; however, fire suppression and landscape fragmentation over many years have produced scrub communities that no longer can support scrub-jay populations. Scrub-jays at Merritt Island National Wildlife Refuge and adjacent government properties constitute a core population within the species' shrinking range. Though the refuge contains over 8,500 hectares of oak scrub, in 2005 only 23 percent was considered to be in optimal condition for scrub-jays. Since 1993 more emphasis has been placed on restoration and maintenance of wildlife habitat, but refuge managers face constraints on the timing and location of burns because of fire and smoke hazards to the nearby Kennedy Space Center and neighboring cities, suburbs, and the Cape Canaveral Air Force Station. Given these constraints, managers must decide what frequency of fire in a collection of management units will best ensure the long-term persistence of the refuge's scrub-jay population. Scrub sites with a long history of fire suppression also require cutting of the scrub to ensure an effective burn. Decisions concerning cutting and prescribed burning are difficult because of incomplete understanding of fire dynamics, plant community succession, and the demographic responses of scrub-jays to environmental factors. Adaptive management identifies management strategies that account for these uncertainties, while using what is learned to adjust and improve scrub management over time.

Tallapoosa River – R.L. Harris Dam

Extensive hydropower development has altered riverine habitats in the southeastern United States, which is a global center of freshwater fish and invertebrate diversity. The Tallapoosa River in east central Alabama is a priority area for aquatic conservation, with a native fish assemblage of 57 species, including 5 species endemic to the Tallapoosa River system. Of these, four fishes and one mussel are considered to be "at risk" by the Fish and Wildlife Service. Fish and invertebrate populations in one of the highest-quality segments of Tallapoosa habitat were threatened with extirpation by extreme low flows, flow instability, and altered temperatures resulting from daily pulsed flow releases for hydropower at the utility-owned R.L. Harris Dam. The Fish and Wildlife Service has been evaluating relicensing of more than 200 dams in the southeastern United States – including the Harris dam – that are licensed by the Federal Energy Regulatory Commission (FERC). Through the Southern Rivers Integrated Science Initiative, the Service has recognized the great need for new approaches to evaluate dam relicensing, and new strategies to mitigate the impacts of dam operations on aquatic communities. Rather than the one-time fixed flow regime typical of FERC relicensing prescriptions, adaptive management has been used on the Tallapoosa since 2005 to allow for the adjustment of flow management based on what is learned from system responses. This project is intended to provide a template for incorporating adaptive management and decision support into the FERC relicensing process.

Red Knots and Horseshoe Crabs

The sandy beaches of Delaware Bay in Delaware and New Jersey are globally important spawning grounds for Atlantic horseshoe crabs and stopover habitat for long-distance migratory shorebirds such as the red knot. Annually, the birds stop in Delaware Bay during May to rest and replenish their energy reserves while migrating from wintering grounds in temperate and tropical regions to breeding grounds in Arctic regions. They stop in the bay to exploit the seasonally superabundant horseshoe crab eggs deposited on the beaches by millions of crabs that spawn during the lunar tides each spring. Throughout the 1990s a growing and unregulated harvest of horseshoe crabs for use as bait in eel and whelk fisheries led to a decline in numbers of spawning crabs. In the late 1990s, monitoring data began to show major declines in red knot abundance. Shorebird scientists and advocacy groups blamed horseshoe crab fishing as the root cause of the red knot decline, while other scientists and horseshoe crab fishermen's groups argued that red knots are not solely reliant on horseshoe crab eggs for food, and that some other environmental factor must be responsible for the decline in red knot numbers. Conservationists called for a complete cessation of horseshoe crab fishing in the Delaware Bay, while others called for moderate regulations to protect the horseshoe crab fishery. Adaptive management was initiated on this contentious issue, with a goal of identifying a sustainable horseshoe crab harvest strategy that protects red knots and enables learning about how the system functions.

Red-Cockaded Woodpeckers in Southeastern Pine Forests

The endangered red-cockaded woodpecker is a cooperatively breeding bird whose social system depends on mature oldgrowth pine forests of the southeastern United States. Family groups, including helpers at the nest, may be as large as nine birds. A woodpecker group roosts and nests in a cluster of living pines in which cavities have been excavated; each bird has its own cavity for roosting. The cluster may include 1 to 30 cavity trees. Preferred cluster sites are mature, parklike pine stands about 4 hectares in area; the group defends a territory of perhaps 80 hectares around the cluster. Birds select very old trees for the excavation of nesting cavities; other habitat requirements include few or no midstory trees and the presence of an adequate understory, but the old-growth condition is the underlying requirement. These habitat conditions were routinely met by the historic disturbances that shaped the pine forests. Red-cockaded woodpeckers once occurred in other forest types from New Jersey to Florida and west to Oklahoma and Missouri, including loblolly pine forests of the Piedmont. The Recovery Plan for the species calls for establishment of primary and secondary populations across different forest types and provinces. One recovery target is the Fish and Wildlife Service's Piedmont National Wildlife Refuge and Chattahoochee–Oconee National Forest complex in central Georgia. These lands came into federal ownership in the 1930s after the collapse of cotton farming in the region, after which forests of mixed loblolly pine and hardwoods have become established. The red-cockaded woodpecker population in this forest complex is the largest in the Piedmont physiographic province. Creation and long-term maintenance of old-growth forest is critical for sustaining this population. Adaptive management is used to account for uncertainty about the maximum attainable amount of old-growth loblolly pine forest, and to make decisions about the harvest strategy to obtain the most old-growth habitat over the long term.

Golden Eagles in Denali

Throughout the Northern Hemisphere, the golden eagle is the pre-eminent diurnal predator of medium-sized birds and mammals in open country. The mountainous regions of Alaska's Denali National Park support the highest nesting density of golden eagles in North America, with undisturbed cliffs for nests that are used over decades or even centuries, and abundant snowshoe hares, ptarmigan, and other prey. Nesting eagles are sensitive to human disturbance, and the National Park Service must limit human presence near nest sites in order to maintain Denali's eagle population. Eagles may occupy any of nearly 100 potential nesting sites across the northeastern part of the park between March and September during the course of their reproductive cycle of nest repair, egg-laying, and rearing eaglets to independence. This means that a large portion of Denali, a premier national wilderness recreation destination during the summer months, could potentially be off limits to hiking and other enjoyment of the park. To reconcile the conflicting demands of maximizing recreational access to as much of the park as possible, and minimizing disturbance of nesting eagles, the national park uses adaptive management to make annual decisions about whether and how much to limit recreational hiking near nesting areas.

Five Rivers Forest Landscape Management Study

The towering forests of the Pacific Northwest, growing over the course of millennia, have shaped the evolution of many species dependent on late-succession and riparian habitat. For example, the marbled murrelet, a coastal seabird, requires mature old-growth forest for nesting; the northern spotted owl, a predatory nocturnal bird, hunts and breeds in old-growth stands; and the Siskiyou Mountains salamander, an endemic amphibian, is found only in deep forests along the Oregon–Washington border. The Northwest Forest Plan revolutionized management of federal lands in the Pacific Northwest to accommodate these and other species, which were thought to be declining as a result of extensive timber production that eliminated old-growth habitats. Management of many forest plantations, which make up about 50 percent of the land area in the central Oregon Coast Range, was redirected from producing timber to growing late-successional stands. Uncertainty was clearly acknowledged by managers, who recognized that no one had ever grown late-successional stands from plantations before. The Forest Service designed a landscape-scale project on 4,800 hectares of the Siuslaw National Forest to address the controversy about whether plantations should be thinned, and to what degree, or whether they should be left to develop on their own. The project implemented adaptive management in comparing three strategies with a standard random-block design. By developing the rationale for all strategies and demonstrating their implementation, this study has already helped change forest management in coastal national forest lands. One of the three strategies, involving wide commercial thinning of existing plantations to speed development of late-successional vegetation structure, was previously controversial and has now become widely accepted.

Adaptive Management of Waterfowl Hunting

Adaptive harvest management was developed to deal explicitly with multiple sources of uncertainty in the regulation of sport waterfowl hunting in North America. Early each year, the Fish and Wildlife Service announces its intent to establish waterfowl hunting regulations and provides the schedule of public rule-making under authority of the Migratory Bird Treaty Act of 1918 (as amended) and other relevant laws. The agency director appoints a Migratory Bird Regulations Committee with representatives of the Waterfowl Flyway Councils, which presides over the process and is responsible for regulatory recommendations. Adaptive harvest management is the framework adopted by the Committee to deal with uncertainty in the regulation of sport waterfowl hunting in North America, including uncontrolled environmental variation, partial control of harvests, and uncertainty concerning waterfowl population dynamics and the impact of harvest. The approach produces optimal regulatory policies that account for each possible combination of breeding population size, environmental conditions, and the current level of understanding. A regulatory choice is identified each year, and post-decision monitoring data are used to update biological understanding for the next year. In this way harvest policy evolves adaptively over time as new knowledge is incorporated.

Biscuit Fire Landscape Management after the Wildfire

Fire-adapted ecosystems were historically maintained in the Pacific Northwest by relatively frequent wildfires of low to moderate intensity. In Oregon's Siskiyou National Forest, an average of 8,000 hectares burned annually until the 1940s, but over the next 50 years that figure fell by almost 90 percent. Between 1940 and 1990, large, plume-driven forest wildfires became uncommon in Oregon and Washington as a result of systematic and effective fire suppression. However, an unintended consequence, the decades-long buildup of dead fuels, probably contributed to recently increasing numbers of very large fires. In 2002, drought, heat, and other climate factors led to a series of Pacific Northwest wildfires culminating in the nation's biggest fire, the Biscuit Complex fire, which consumed about 200,000 hectares of forest. The magnitude of the Biscuit fire and new mandates from the Northwest Forest Plan regarding late-succession and riparian habitats created much uncertainty about the most appropriate forest management after a wildfire. Rather than choosing the typical method of "salvage" logging and replanting, Forest Service researchers helped develop a peer-reviewed study plan that was adopted in the final Record of Decision for the Biscuit Fire Recovery Project. Adaptive management is being used to compare three competent management strategies on 14,500 hectares of land in the Rogue River–Siskiyou National Forest and Medford District of the Bureau of Land Management, in order to understand better how to manage forests after large wildfires.

Laysan Duck Translocation

The Laysan duck represents a great success in endangered species recovery. It is a critically endangered dabbling duck endemic to the Hawaiian islands; it became confined to Laysan Island after humans introduced rats to the Hawaiian islands. The ducks do not disperse from Laysan today, but sub-fossil remains show that the species was once widespread in the Hawaiian islands. Low abundance, random disasters, and the limited carrying capacity of the fragile ecosystems on tiny islands are the main threats to its persistence. Since the severe contraction of the range from the main Hawaiian islands, random events that have already occurred include the accidental introduction of noxious competitors (rabbits), extreme weather (droughts, hurricanes), and disease epizootics (parasitic nematode, avian botulism). Twice during the last century, the single population was pushed to the brink of extinction (in 1911, only 11 individuals remained). Living on relatively low-lying islands, this species is now susceptible to climate change through sea-level rise and shifts in suitable climatic conditions. Creation of other wild populations within the duck's former range became a high priority in the Fish and Wildlife Service's Laysan Duck Recovery Plan. During 2004–2005, an initial translocation to Midway Atoll, part of the National Wildlife Refuge System, established another breeding population. Additional populations on different islands are planned in the northwestern Hawaiian islands, part of the Papahānaumokuākea Marine National Monument, which is jointly managed by the Service and the National Oceanic and Atmospheric Administration, in close coordination with the state of Hawaii. Adaptive management will guide the selection of the best islands for further translocations.

Northwest Forest Plan

The northern spotted owl is a nocturnal hunter of flying squirrels, birds, and other prey deep in ancient stands of conifers in the Pacific Northwest. It requires old-growth forest habitat for breeding and foraging. As a federally listed threatened species, it became the focal point of a national debate over the cumulative effects of timber harvesting and losses of late-successional stands on federal lands in the Pacific Northwest. A 1991 injunction halted timber harvest on 9.7 million hectares of federal lands in the owl's range. President Clinton intervened in 1993 to set up a science-based forest ecosystem management assessment team that helped frame a Record of Decision, creating the Northwest Forest Plan to revamp management of these lands. Court and planning documents acknowledged high levels of uncertainty and established adaptive management as the cornerstone of this plan. Following a 10-year period of monitoring forests in 10 adaptive management areas delineated in the plan, evaluation of evidence in a broad and integrative context helped federal agency regional executives to improve the Northwest's regional adaptive management framework and to assess priority questions by means of adaptive management concepts. The regional framework helps to pull together individual adaptive management efforts of the Northwest Forest Plan, such as the Five Rivers and Biscuit landscape projects as well as other research activities, and to interpret them together in a formal process aimed at improving land-management decision making at the regional level.

Glossary

Adaptive Decision Making

Decision making that accounts for what is uncertain as well as what is known about the processes that influence natural resource behavior through time and the influence of management on resource changes. Adaptive decision making seeks to reduce this uncertainty and thereby improve management through enhanced understanding of management effects.

Adaptive Management

This term is used interchangeably with adaptive decision making.

Bayes' Rule

A technique used to propagate structural uncertainty through time; the technique combines measures of uncertainty at each point in time with data from post-decision monitoring to produce new measures for the next time.

Climate Change Adaptation

Adaptation in natural or human systems to a new or changing environment. Adaptation refers to adjustments in natural or human systems that are intended to reduce vulnerability to actual or anticipated climate change, or to exploit opportunities arising from that change.

Climate Change Mitigation

Actions resulting in reductions in the degree or intensity of greenhouse gas emissions. Sometimes referred to as abatement.

Decision Problem

In natural resources, a problem that requires managers to make a decision, once or repeatedly, that will influence resource conditions or processes. In adaptive management, the decision problem involves iterative decision making, with the opportunity to learn through time and adjust management strategies on the basis of what is learned.

Ecosystem Services

Goods and services that create value for human users and are derived from ecosystem processes such as nutrient recycling, climate regulation, and maintenance of biodiversity. Examples of ecosystem services include clean drinking water, flood risk reduction, pollination of crops, and decomposition of wastes. Examples of marketable goods provided by ecosystems include lumber and seafood.

Estimation

The aggregation of field data into measures of resource attributes. Examples include means, variances, and correlation coefficients computed with sample data. Multiple estimators are always available for any resource attribute, and the choice of which particular estimator to use is based on features such as statistical bias and precision.

Experimentation

The imposition of treatments on subjects or experimental units for the explicit purpose of learning about treatment effects by observing outcomes. Ideally, experimentation involves random allocation of treatments to experimental units, replication of treatments, and the use of controls for comparative purposes.

Experimental Management

The use of management interventions for the purpose of understanding the effects of management. Interventions are used as experimental treatments, ideally (but infrequently) involving randomization, replication, and experimental control.

Hypothesis

A suggested but unconfirmed explanation of observed patterns. Hypotheses can take many forms, such as a hypothesized magnitude of a resource attribute or a hypothesized mathematical relationship between attributes. Hypotheses are tested by comparison with field data.

Management by Experiment

An approach to management that recognizes management interventions as experiments, by means of which understanding can be enhanced as management proceeds over time.

Management Action

An action that affects a managed system, and is taken as a result of a management decision. In the context of natural resources, management actions typically influence the status of resources or the processes that control resource dynamics.

Management Alternative

A potential management action. In sequential management, a management action is selected at each point in time from an identified set of management alternatives. The set of management alternatives constrains and influences the choice of a management strategy.

Management Decision

A decision to take a management action. In adaptive management, decision making usually is driven by management objectives, with active stakeholder involvement. Adaptive decision making takes into account both the current status of resources and the level of understanding about them.

Management Option

This term is used interchangeably with management alternative.

Management Strategy

A prescription of management actions designed to meet management objectives. In the context of adaptive management, a management strategy describes management actions to be taken at specific times. At a particular point in time, the action that is prescribed depends on the current resource status and the level of understanding about resource dynamics. Management strategies are often expressed in terms of resource thresholds, on either side of which a different action is to be taken.

Model

Any representation, whether verbal, diagrammatic, or mathematical, of an object or phenomenon. Natural resource models usually characterize resource systems in terms of their status and change over time. Models incorporate hypotheses about resource structure and function, and they generate predictions about the effects of management actions.

Non-Stationarity

Directional change in resource structure and function over time. Natural resource systems with ecological processes and parameters that vary directionally over time are non-stationary. Similarly, management strategies that vary through time are non-stationary. Natural resources subject to long-term, directional environmental change are likely to exhibit non-stationary behaviors. As an example of directional (non-stationary) environmental change, a stable (stationary) pattern of fluctuation in annual rainfall may become non-stationary because a warming climate induces fluctuations with increasing extremes. In such a case, both minimum rainfall and maximum rainfall would trend directionally upward (or downward) year by year.

Objective

A desired outcome or performance measure that expresses stakeholder values and serves to guide natural resource decision making and the evaluation of success.

Resilience

The ability of a system to absorb disturbances and still retain the same basic structure and functions. A resilient system is flexible and forgiving of external shocks. As resilience declines, the magnitude of shocks from which the system cannot recover becomes smaller and smaller. Management for resilience seeks flexible system behaviors that can deliver desired ecosystem goods and services on a sustained basis.

Stakeholders

Individuals and organizations (e.g., managers, scientists, private citizens, non-governmental organizations) with a vested interest in a shared enterprise. Interests can include an expectation of received benefit, a perceived threat, a prior investment of time or resources, or values shared with others associated with the enterprise. Active engagement of stakeholders promotes the successful implementation of adaptive management.

Sustainability

The capacity to endure over an extended time. Sustainable resource systems retain their structure, functions, and ability to provide ecological services. Resource management that maintains long-term resource productivity constitutes sustainable management. Sustainability is closely tied to the concept of system resilience.

Threshold

The limiting value of a resource attribute that triggers a change in management actions. Management strategies often include thresholds, such that one action is specified for resource values less than the threshold and a different action is specified for resource values greater than the threshold.

REFERENCES

Allen, G. M. & Gould, E. M. Jr. (1986). Complexity, wickedness, and public forests. *Journal of Forestry*, *84*, 20-23.

Allen, W. J., Bosch, O. J. H., Kilvington, M. J., Harley, D. & Brown, I. (2001). Monitoring and adaptive management: Addressing social and organisational issues to improve information sharing. *Natural Resources Forum*, *25*, 225-233.

Allenby, B. R. & Richards, D. J. (1994). *The Greening of Industrial Ecosystems., Washington*, DC: National Academy Press.

Argyris, C. & Shon, D. (1978). Org*anization Learning: A Theory of Action Learning.* Reading, MA: Addison-Wesley.

Ashworth, M. J. (1982). *Feedback Design of Systems with Significant Uncertainty.* Chichester, UK: Research Studies Press.

Ben-Haim, Y. (2002). *Info-gap Decision Theory: Decisions Under Uncertainty,* 2nd ed. New York: Academic Press.

Beverton, R. J. H. & Holt, S. J. (1957). *On the Dynamics of Exploited Fish Populations.* London: Her Majesty's Stationery Office.

Bormann, B. T., Cunningham, P. G. & Gordon, J. C. (1996). Best management practices, adaptive management, or both? In *Proceedings of the 1995 National Society of American Foresters Convention.* Conference held at Portland, ME.

Bormann, B. T., Haynes, R. W. & Martin, J. R. (2007). Adaptive management of forest ecosystems: Did some rubber hit the road? *Bioscience*, *57*, 186-191.

Bormann, B. T. & Kiester, A. R. (2004. Options forestry: Acting on uncertainty. *Journal of Forestry* 102:22-27. Burgman, M. (2005). *Risks and Decisions for Conservation and Environmental Management.* Cambridge: Cambridge University Press.

Conover, D. O. & Munch, S. B. (2002). Sustaining fisheries yields over evolutionary time scales. *Science*, *297*, 94-96.

Endter-Wada, J., Blahna, D., Krannich, R. & Brunson, M. (1998. A framework for understanding social science contributions to ecosystem management. *Ecological Applications*, *8*, 891-904.

Failing, E., Horn, G. & Higgens, P. (2004). Using expert judgment and stakeholder values to evaluate adaptive management options. *Ecology and Society*, *9*, 13. http://www.ecologyandsocieity.org/vol9/iss1/13.

Freeman, D. M. (2010). *Implementing the Endangered Species Act on the Platte Basin Water Commons*. Boulder: University of Colorado Press.

Fulmer, W. E. (2000). *Shaping the Adaptive Organization: Landscapes, Learning, and Leadership in Volatile Times*. New York: AMACOM.

Graybill, F. A. (1976). *Theory and Application of the General Linear Model*. North Scituate, MA: Duxbury Press.

Gregory R. D. & Keeney, R. L. (2002. Making smarter environmental management decisions. *Journal of the American Water Resources Association*, *38*, 1601-1612.

Gregory R, Ohlson, D. & Arvai, J. (2006). Deconstructing adaptive management: Criteria for applications to environmental management. *Ecological Applications*, *16*, 2411-2425.

Gunderson, L. (1999*a*). Resilience, flexibility and adaptive management – antidotes for spurious certitude? *Conservation Ecology*, *3*, 7. http://www.consecol.org/vol3/iss1/art7

Gunderson, L. (1999*b*). Stepping back: Assessing for understanding in complex regional systems. In K. N. Johnson, F. Swanson, M. Herring, and S. Greene. (eds.). *Bioregional Assessments: Science at the Crossroads of Management and Policy*. Washington, DC: Island Press.

Gunderson, L. H. & Holling, C. S. (2002). *Panarchy: Understanding Transformations in Human and Natural Systems*. Washington, DC: Island Press.

Gunderson, L. H., Holling, C. S. & Light, S. S. (eds.). (1995). *Barriers and Bridges to the Renewal of Ecosystems and Institutions*. New York: Columbia University Press.

Halbert, C. L. (1993). How adaptive is adaptive management? Implementing adaptive management in Washington state and British Columbia. *Reviews in Fisheries Science*, *1*, 261-283.

Heller, N. E. & Zavaleta, E. S. (2009). Biodiversity management in the face of climate change: A review of 22 years of recommendations. *Biological Conservation*, *142*, 14-32.

Hilborn, R. (1992). Can fisheries agencies learn from experience? *Fisheries*, *17*, 6-14.

Holling, C. S. (ed.). (1978). *Adaptive Environmental Assessment and Management*. Chichester, UK: Wiley.

Holling, C. S., Gunderson, L. H. & Walters, C. J. (1994. The structure and dynamics of the Everglades system: Guidelines for ecosystem restoration. In S. Davis and J. Ogden (eds.). *Everglades: The Ecosystem and its Restoration*. Delray Beach, FL: St. Lucie Press.

Jager, H. I., & Rose, K. A. (2003). Designing optimal flow patterns for fall chinook salmon in a Central Valley, California, river. *North American Journal of Fisheries Management*, *23*, 1-21.

Johnson, B. L. (1999). Introduction to adaptive management: Scientifically sound, socially challenged? *Conservation Ecology*, *3*, 8. http://www.consecol.org/Journal/vol3/iss1/art10

Johnson, J. A., Kendall, W. L. & Dubovsky, J. A. (2002). Conditions and limitations on learning in the adaptive management of mallard harvests. *Wildlife Society Bulletin*, *30*, 176-185.

Knutson, M. G., & Heglund, P. J. (2011). Resource managers rise to the challenge of climate change. In J. L. Belant and E. Beever (eds.). *Ecological Consequences of Climate Change: Mechanisms, Conservation, and Management.* New York: Taylor and Francis.

Knutson, M., Laskowski, H., Moore, C., Lonsdorf, E., Lor, S. & Stevenson, L. (2010). Defensible decision making: Harnessing the power of adaptive resource management. *The Wildlife Professional, 4*, 58-62.

Lee, P. M. (1989. *Bayesian Statistics: An Introduction.* London: Edward Arnold.

Lee, K. N. (1993. *Compass and Gyroscope: Integrating Science and Politics for the Environment.* Washington, DC: Island Press.

Lee, K. N. (1999). Appraising adaptive management. *Conservation Ecology, 3*, 3. http://www.consecol.org/Journal/vol3/iss2/art3/

Lessard, G. (1998). *An adaptive approach to planning and decision making . Landscape and Urban Planning, 40*, 81-87.

Le Treut, H., Somerville, R., Cubasch, U., Ding, Y., Mauritzen, C., Mokssit, A., Peterson, T., & Prather, M. (2007). Historical Overview of climate change. In S. Solomon, D. Qin, M. Manning, Z. Chen, M. Marquis, K. B. Averyt, M. Tignor, and H. L. Miller (eds.). *Climate Change 2007: The Physical Science Basis. Contribution of Working Group I to the Fourth Assessment Report of the Intergovernmental Panel on Climate Change.* Cambridge: Cambridge University Press.

Levine, J. (2004). Adaptive management in river restoration: Theory vs. practice in western North America. Water Resources Center Archives. Restoration of Rivers and Streams. http://repositories.cdlib.org/wrca/restoration/levine or http://repositories.cdlib.org/cgi/viewcontent. cgi?article=1039&context=wrca.

Lubow, B. C. (1997). Adaptive stochastic dynamic programming (ASDP): Supplement to SDP user's guide, version 2. 0. Fort Collins, CO: Colorado Cooperative Fish and Wildlife Resources Unit, Colorado State University.

Ludwig, D., Hilborn, R. & Walters, C. (1993). Uncertainty, resource exploitation, and conservation: Lessons learned from history. *Science, 260*, 17-36.

Marmorek, D. R., Robinson, D. C. E., Murray, C. & Greig, L. (2006). Enabling adaptive forest management – final report. Vancouver, BC: National Commission on Science for Sustainable Forestry.

Martin, F. W., Pospahala, R. S. & Nichols, J. D. (1979). Assessment and population management of North American migratory birds. In J. Cairns, Jr., G. P. Patil, and W. E. Walters (eds.). *Environmental Biomonitoring, Assessment, Prediction, and Management – Certain Case Studies and Related Quantitative Issues.* Fairland, MD: International Publishing House.

McFadden, J. E., Hiller, T. L. & Tyre, A. J. (2011). Evaluating the efficacy of adaptive management approaches: Is there a formula for success? *Journal of Environmental Management, 92*, 1354-1359.

McConnaha, W. E. & Paquet, P. J. (1996). Adaptive strategies for the management of ecosystems: The Columbia River experience. *American Fisheries Science Symposium, 16*, 410-421.

McLain, D. & Lee, R. G. (1996). Adaptive management: Promises and pitfalls. *Environmental Management, 20*, 437-448.

Melis, T. S., Martell, S. J. D., Coggins, L. G. Jr., Pine, W. E. III & Anderson, M. E. (2006). Adaptive management of the Colorado River ecosystem below the Glen Canyon Dam,

Arizona: Using science and modeling to resolve uncertainty in river management. In *Proceedings of the Conference on Adaptive Management of Water Resources.* Middleburg, VA: American Water Resources Association. http://www.awra.org/proceedings/cdrom. html

Michael, D. N. (1995). Barriers and bridges to learning in a turbulent human ecology. In L. H. Gunderson, C. S. Holling, and S. S. Light (eds.). *Barriers and Bridges to the Renewal of Ecosystems and Institutions.* New York: Columbia University Press.

Miller, A. (1999). *Environmental Problem Solving: Psychosocial Barriers to Adaptive Change.* New York: SpringerVerlag.

Moore, C. T. & Conroy, M. J. (2006). Optimal regeneration planning for old-growth forests: Addressing scientific uncertainty in endangered species recovery through adaptive management. *Forest Science, 52*, 155-172.

Moore, C. T. & Kendall, W. L. (2004). Costs of detection bias in index-based population monitoring. *Animal Biodiversity and Conservation, 27*, 287-296.

Moore, C. T., Lonsdorf, E. V., Knutson, M. G., Laskowski, H. P. & Lor, S. K. (2011). Adaptive management in the U. S. National Wildlife Refuge System: Science–management partnerships for conservation delivery. *Journal of Environmental Management, 92*, 1395-1402.

Morghan, K. J. R., Sheley, R. L. & Svejcar, T. J. (2006). Successful adaptive management – the integration of research and management. *Rangeland Ecology and Management, 59*, 216-219.

National Research Council. (2004). *Adaptive Management for Water Resources Planning.* Washington, DC: National Academies Press.

National Research Council. (2005). *Valuing Ecosystem Services.* Washington, DC: National Academies Press.

National Ecological Assessment Team. (2006). Strategic habitat conservation: Final report. Reston, VA, and Washington, DC: U. S. Geological Survey and U. S. Fish and Wildlife Service.

Nichols, J. D., Koneff, M. D., Heglund, P. J., Knutson, M. G., Seamans, M. E., Lyons, J. E., Morton, J. M., Jones, M. T., Boomer, G. S. & Williams, B. K. (2011). Climate change, uncertainty and natural resource management. *Journal of Wildlife Management, 75*, 6-18.

Nichols, J. D. & Williams, B. K. (2006). Monitoring for conservation. *Trends in Ecology and Evolution* 21:668-673. Norton, B. G, (2005). *Sustainability: A Philosophy of Adaptive Ecosystem Management.* Chicago: University of Chicago Press.

O'Donnell, T. K. & Galat, D. L. (2008). Evaluating success criteria and project monitoring in river enhancement within an adaptive management framework. *Environmental Management, 41*, 90-105.

Peterman, R. M. & Peters, C. N. (1998). Decision analysis: Taking uncertainties into account in forest resource management. In V. Sit and B. Taylor (eds.). *Statistical Methods for Adaptive Management Studies.* Land Management Handbook 42. Victoria, BC: British Columbia Ministry of Forests.

Peterson, G. D., Carpenter, S. R. & Block, W. A. (2003). Uncertainty and the management of multistate ecosystems: An apparently rational route to collapse. *Ecology, 84*, 1403-1411.

Popper, K. R. (1968). *The Logic of Scientific Discovery*, 2nd ed. New York: Harper and Row.

Quigley, T. M. & Arbelbide, S. J. (eds.). (1997). *An assessment of ecosystem components in the interior Columbia basin and portions of the Klamath and Great Basins*, vol. *1.*

General technical report PNW-GTR-405. Portland, OR: U. S. Department of Agriculture, Forest Service.

Rauscher, H. M. (1999). Ecosystem management decision support for federal forests in the United States: A review. *Forest Ecology and Management*, *114*, 173-197.

Rapp, V. (2008). Northwest Forest Plan – the first 10 years (1994–2003): First-decade results of the Northwest Forest Plan. General technical report PNW-GTR-720. Portland, OR: U. S. Department of Agriculture, Forest Service.

Reeves, G. H., Williams, J. E., Burnett, K. M. & Gallo, K. (2006). The aquatic conservation strategy of the Northwest Forest Plan. *Conservation Biology*, *20*, 319-329.

Regan, H. M., Colyvan, M. & Burgman, M. (2002). A taxonomy and treatment of uncertainty for ecology and conservation biology. *Ecological Applications*, *12*, 618-628.

Resilience Alliance web site. Adaptive management. http://www.resalliance.org/index.php?id=1245&sr=1&type=pop

Rodgers, W. H. (1994). *Environmental Law*, 2nd ed. St. Paul, MN: West Publishing.

Rogers, K. (1998). Managing science/management partnerships: A challenge of adaptive management. *Conservation Ecology*, *2*, 2. http://www.consecol.org/Journal/vol3/iss1/art10.

Salafsky, N., Margoluis, R. & Redford, K. (2001). *Adaptive Management: A Tool for Conservation Practitioners.* Washington, DC: Biodiversity Support Program. http://www.worldwildlife.org/bsp/

Schreiber, E. S. G., Bearlin, A. R., Nicol, S. J. & Todd, C. R. (2004). Adaptive management: A synthesis of current understanding and effective application. *Ecological Management and Restoration*, *5*, 177-182.

Senge, P. M. (1990). *The Fifth Discipline: The Art and Practice of the Learning Organization.* New York: Currency Doubleday.

Shea, K., Possingham, H. P., Murdoch, W. W. & Roush, R. (2002). Active adaptive management in insect pest and weed control: Intervention with a plan for learning. *Ecological Applications*, *12*, 927-936.

Smith, R. I., Blohm, R. J., Kelly, S. T. & Reynolds, R. E. (1989). Review of data bases for managing duck harvests. *Transactions, North American Wildlife and Natural Resources Conference*, *54*, 537-544.

Stankey, G. H. (2003). Adaptive management at the regional scale: Breakthrough innovation or mission impossible? A report on an American experience. In P. B. Wilson and A. Curtis (eds.). *Proceedings of the 2002 Fenner Conference on the Environment: Agriculture for the Australian Environment.* Conference held at Charles Sturt University, Alsbury, Western Australia.

Stankey, G. H., Bormann, B. T., Ryan, C., Shindler, B., Sturtevant, V., Clark, R. N. & Philpot, C. (2003). Adaptive management and the northwest forest plan: Rhetoric and reality. *Journal of Forestry*, *101*, 40-46.

Stankey, G. H., & Clark, R. N. (2006). Adaptive management: Facing up to the challenges. In R. W. Haynes, B. T. Bormann, D. C. Lee and J. R. Martin (eds.). Northwest Forest Plan – the first ten years (1994–2003): Synthesis of monitoring and research results. General technical report PNW GTR 651. Portland, OR: U. S. Department of Agriculture, Forest Service.

Stankey, G. H., Clark, R. N. & Bormann, B. T. (2005). Adaptive management of natural resources: Theory, concepts, and management institutions. General technical report PNW-GTR-654. Portland, OR: U. S. Department of Agriculture, Forest Service.

U. S. Fish and Wildlife Service, (2006). Strategic Habitat Conservation: A report from the National Ecological Assessment Team. Washington, DC: U. S. Fish and Wildlife Service.

U. S. Geological Survey, (2008). Science plan for potential 2008 experimental high flow at Glen Canyon Dam. Flagstaff, AZ: Southwest Biological Science Center, Grand Canyon Monitoring and Research Center.

Walker, B., & Salt, D. (2006). *Resilience Thinking: Sustaining Ecosystems and People in a Changing World.* Washington, DC: Island Press.

Walters, C. J. (1986). *Adaptive Management of Renewable Resources.* Caldwell, NJ: Blackburn Press.

Walters, C. (1997). Challenges in adaptive management of riparian and coastal ecosystems. *Conservation Biology*, *1*, 1, http://www.consecol.org/vol1/iss2/art1

Walters, C. J. (2007). Is adaptive management helping to solve fisheries problems? *Ambio*, *36*, 304-307.

Walters, C. & Green, R. (1997). Valuation of experimental management options for ecological systems. *Journal of Wildlife Management*, *61*, 987-1006.

Walters, C. J. & Hilborn, R. (1978). Ecological optimization and adaptive management. *Annual Review of Ecology and Systematics*, *9*, 157-188.

Walters, C. J. & Holling, C. S. (1990). Large-scale management experiments and learning by doing. *Ecology*, *71*, 2060-2068.

Weinstein, M. P., Balletto, J. H., Teal, J. M. & Ludwig, D. F. (1997). Success criteria and adaptive management for a largescale wetland restoration project. *Wetlands Ecology and Management*, *4*, 111-127.

Wildavsky, A. (1988). *Searching for Safety.* New Brunswick, NJ: Transaction Publishers.

Williams, B. K. (1996). Adaptive optimization of renewable natural resources: Solution algorithms and a computer program. *Ecological Modelling*, *93*, 101-111.

Williams, B. K. (1997*a*). Logic and science in wildlife biology. *Journal of Wildlife Management*, *61*, 1007-1015.

Williams, B. K. (1997*b*). Approaches to the management of waterfowl under uncertainty. *Wildlife Society Bulletin*, *25*, 714-720.

Williams, B. K. (2001). Uncertainty, learning, and optimization in wildlife management. *Environmental and Ecological Statistics*, *8*, 269-288.

Williams, B. K, (2006). Adaptive harvest management: Where we are, how we got here, and what we have learned thus far. *Transactions, North American Wildlife and Natural Resources Conference*, *71*, 259-274.

Williams, B. K. (2009). Markov processes in natural resources management: Observability and uncertainty. *Ecological Modelling*, *220*, 830-840.

Williams, B. K. (2011). Adaptive management of natural resources: Framework and issues. *Journal of Environmental Management*, *92*, 1346-1353.

Williams, B. K, (2011*b*). Passive and active adaptive management: Approaches and an example. *Journal of Environmental Management*, *92*, 1371-1378.

Williams, B. K., & F. A. Johnson, (1995). Adaptive management and the regulation of waterfowl harvests. *Wildlife Society Bulletin*, *23*, 430-436.

Williams, B. K., Nichols, J. D. & Conroy, M. J. (2002). *Analysis and Management of Animal Populations.* San Diego, CA: Academic Press.

Williams, B. K., Szaro, R. C. & Shapiro, C. D. (2007). Adaptive management: The U. S. Department of the Interior technical guide. Washington, DC: U. S. Department of the Interior.

Williams, J. W. & Jackson, S. T. (2007). Novel climates, no-analog communities, and ecological surprises. *Frontiers in Ecology, 5*, 475-482.

Williams, R. N. (2006). *Return to the River: Restoring Salmon to the Columbia River.* Amsterdam: Elsevier.

Wissmar, R. C. & Bisson, P. A. (eds.), (2003). *Strategies for Restoring River Ecosystems: Sources of Variability and Uncertainty in Natural and Managed Systems.* Bethesda, MD: American Fisheries Society.

Wondolleck, J. & Yaffe, S. (2000). *Making Collaboration Work: Lessons from Innovation in Natural Resource Management.* Washington, DC: Island Press.

References for the Examples

Laysan duck translocation

Reynolds, M., McGowan, C., Converse, S. J., Mattson, B., Hatfield, J. S., McClung, A., Mehrhoff, L., Walters, J. R. & Uyehara, K. (2011). Trading of short-term and long-term risk: Minimizing the threat of Laysan Duck extinction from catastrophes and sea-level rise. Report to the National Conservation Training Center Decision Analysis Training Program http://training.fws.gov/CSP/Resources/Decision_Analysis/jan_10/presentations/laysan_duck/final_report.pdf

U.S. Geological Survey. Translocation of endangered Laysan ducks to Midway Atoll National Wildlife refuge (2004-5). U.S. Geological Survey fact sheet no. USGS FS 2005-3128. http://biology.usgs.gov/pierc/Current%20News/Laysan%20Fact%20Sheet%20Final%20LoRes.pdf

U.S. Fish and Wildlife Service. Pacific Region recovery leader – Laysan duck Midway translocation team. http://www.fws.gov/pacific/ecoservices/endangered/recovery/LaysanDuckTeam.htm

Native prairie restoration in the northern Great Plains

Gannon, J. J., Moore, C. T. & Shaffer, T. L. (2010). An adaptive approach to invasive plant management on Fish and Wildlife Service – owned native prairies in the northern Great Plains: Decision support under uncertainty. Paper presented at the Ecological Society of America annual meeting, Pittsburgh, PA. http://eco.confex.com/eco/2010/techprogram/P24553.htm

Gleason, R. A., Euliss, N. H., Hubbard, D. E. & Duffy, W. G. (2003). Effects of sediment load on emergence of aquatic invertebrates and plants from wetland soil egg and seed banks. *Wetlands, 23*, 26-34.

Robertson, K. The tallgrass prairie in Illinois. Illinois Natural History Survey. http://www.inhs.illinois.edu/~kenr/prairi-erestoration.html

Endangered mussel translocation

Pennsylvania Department of Conservation and Natural Resources. Northern riffleshell *Epiblastoma torulosa rangiana.* http://www.dcnr.state.pa.us/wrcp/rif.aspx

U.S. Fish and Wildlife Service. Northern riffleshell translocation to the Big Darby Creek in Franklin County, Ohio. http://www.fws.gov/midwest/endangered/esday/2009nriffleshell.html

Wyoming Landscape Conservation Initiative

Bureau of Land Management. Wyoming Landscape Conservation Initiative web site. http://www.wlci.gov

New England shrub habitat and New England cottontails

U.S. Fish and Wildlife Service. New England cottontail *Sylvilagus transitionalis.* http://www.fws.gov/northeast/pdf/necotton.fs.pdf

Etowah River endangered stream fishes

Peterson, J., Moore, C., Wenger, S., Kennedy, K., Irwin, E. & Freeman, M. (2007). Adaptive management applied to aquatic natural resources. In *Proceedings of the 2007 Georgia Water Resources Conference.* Conference held at the University of Georgia.

Wenger, S., Freeman, M. C., Fowler, L. A., Freeman, B. J. & Peterson, J. Y. (2010). Conservation planning for imperiled aquatic species in an urbanizing environment. *Landscape Urban Planning*, *77*, 11-21.

Blanca Wetlands

Bureau of Land Management, (2009). South San Luis Lakes wetland restoration project environmental assessment. Bureau of Land Management report no. DOI-BLM-CO-140-2010-009-EA. http://www.blm.gov/pgdata/etc/medialib/blm/co/field_offices/slvplc/Upload_Files.Par.51774.File.dat/SSL_Final_EA.pdf

Rondeau, R. J. Level 4 Potential Conservation Area (PCA) report. Blanca Wetlands, site code S.USCOHP*2551. Colorado Natural Heritage Program, Colorado State University.

Cape Cod National Seashore wind turbines

National Park Service. Cape Cod National Seashore. http://www.nps.gov/caco

Prairie pothole restoration

Prairie Pothole Joint Venture web site. http://www.ppjv.org

U.S. Fish and Wildlife Service. Learning on the wing – wetlands, the vital link. http://www.fws.gov/r5mnwr/lotw/wetlands.html

U.S. Geological Survey Northern Prairie Wildlife Research Center. Wetlands of the prairie pothole region: Invertebrate species composition, ecology, and management. http://www.npwrc.usgs.gov/resource/wetlands/pothole/prairie.htm

Las Cienegas

Bureau of Land Management. Las Cienegas National Conservation Area. http://www.blm.gov/az/st/en/prog/blm_special_areas/ncarea/lascienegas.html

Glen Canyon Dam

Bureau of Reclamation. Glen Canyon Dam Adaptive Management Program web site. http://www.gcdamp.gov U.S.Geological Survey. Grand Canyon Monitoring and Research Center web site. http://www.gcmrc.gov

Agriculture experimentation

Cochran, W. G. & Cox, G. M. (1957). *Experiment Designs*, 2nd ed. New York: John Wiley.

Columbia River chinook salmon

Federal Energy Regulatory Commission. (2004). Hanford Reach fall chinook protection program executed agreement. http://www.nwdwc.usace.army.mil/tmt/documents/wmp/2007/draft/app5.pdf

Lukas, J. (1999). A summary of anadromous fish studies and protection, mitigation and enhancement action implemented by Grant County PUD. Public Utility District No. 2 of Grant County, WA. http://www.gcpud.org/pudDocuments/naturalResourcesDocs/disk2/GCPUDFLA2D/Technical%20Appendices/E4-Fish%20Resources/E4A_Sum_Ana_Fish_PME_Act_FLA.pdf

Sierra Nevada fire fuel treatments

Sierra Nevada Adaptive Management Project web site. http://snamp.cnr.berkeley.edu

Center for Fire Research and Outreach. (2007). Newsletter volume 1, Issue 1. http://firecenter.berkeley.edu

Collins, B. M., Stephens, S. L., Moghaddas, J. J. & Battles, J. (2010). Challenges and approaches in planning fuel treatments across fire-excluded forested landscapes. *Journal of Forestry*, *108*, 24-31.

Great Barrier Reef marine reserve management

McCook, L. J., Ayling, T., Cappo, M., Choat, H., Evans, R. D., De Freitas, D. M., Heupel, M., Highes, T. P., Jones, G. P., Mapstone, B., Marsh, H., Mills, M., Molloy, F. J., Pitcher, C. R., Pressey, R. L., Russ, G. R., Sutton, S., Sweatman, H., Tobin, R., Wachenfeld, D. R. & Williamson, D. H. (2010). Adaptive management of the Great Barrier Reef: A globally significant demonstration of the benefits of networks of marine reserves. *Proceedings of the National Academy of Sciences* Early Edition http://www.pnas.org/cgi/doi/10.1073/pnas.0909335107

Florida Everglades

Comprehensive Everglades Restoration Plan Adaptive Management Steering Committee and Writing Team. (2006). Comprehensive Everglades restoration plan adaptive management strategy. http://www.evergladesplan.org/pm/recover/recover_docs/am/rec_am_stategy_brochure.pdf

Tallapoosa River dam

Irwin, E. R. & Kennedy, K. D. M. (2008). Engaging stakeholders for adaptive management using structured decision analysis. Paper presented at the Third Interagency Conference on Research in the Watersheds, Estes Park, CO. http://pubs.usgs.gov/sir/2009/5049/pdf/Irwin.pdf

Irwin, E. R. & Freeman, M. C. (2002). Proposal for adaptive management to conserve biotic integrity in a regulated segment of the Tallapoosa River, Alabama, U.S.A. *Conservation Biology*, *16*, 1212-1222.

Kennedy, K. D., Irwin, E. R., Freeman, M. C. & Peterson, J. Development of a decision support tool and procedures for evaluating dam operations in the southeastern United States. Final report to the U.S. Geological Survey and the U.S. Fish and Wildlife Service. http://www.rivermanagement.org/decision_support_final_report.pdf

Tallapoosa River adaptive management project web site. Adaptive management of the R.L. Harris Dam and the Tallapoosa River. http://www.rivermanagement.org

Red knots and horseshoe crabs

Breese, G., Smith, D., Nichols, J., Lyons, J., Hecht, A., Clark, N., Michels, S., Millard, M., Scherer, A., Spear, B., Brewer, D. C., Starfield, A. M. & Runge, M. C. (2007). Application of structured decision making to multi-species management of horseshoe crab and shorebird populations in Delaware Bay. Case study from the Structured Decision Making Workshop held 9-13 July 2007 at the National Conservation Training Center, Shepherdstown,WV. http://training.fws.gov/CSP/Resources/Decision_Analysis/July%2007/HSC_SHBD_Final_Report.pdf

McGowan, C. P., Smith, D. R., Sweka, J. A., Martin, J., Nichols, J. D., Wong, R., Lyons, J. E., Niles, L. J., Kalasz, K., Brust, J., Klopfer, M. & Spear, B. (2009). A framework for adaptive management of horseshoe crab harvest in the Delaware Bay constrained by red knot conservation. Report to the Atlantic States Marine Fisheries Commission. http://www.asmfc.org/horseshoeCrab.htm

Southeastern pine forests and red-cockaded woodpeckers

U.S. Fish and Wildlife Service. Red-cockaded woodpecker recovery. http://www.fws.gov/rcwrecovery/rcw.html

Golden eagles in Denali

McIntyre, C., Steenhof, K., Kochert, M. N. & Collopy. M. W. Long-term golden eagle studies in Denali National Park and Preserve. http://environment.unr.edu/contact/CollopyPubs/GoldenEagles.pdf

National Park Service. Golden eagle *(Aquila chrysaetos)*chrysaetos.htm

Biscuit Fire landscape management after the wildfire

Bormann, B. T. & Stankey, G. H. (2009). Crisis as a positive role in implementing adaptive management after the Biscuit Fire, Pacific Northwest, U.S.A. C. Allen, and G.H. Stankey (eds.). *Adaptive Management of Natural Resources and Environments: A Practitioner's Handbook.* New York: Springer.

Northwest Forest Plan

Forest Ecosystem Management Assessment Team. (1993). Forest ecosystem management: An ecological, economic, and social assessment. Portland, OR: U.S. Department of Agriculture, Forest Service, U.S. Department of Commerce, National Oceanic and Atmospheric Administration, U.S. Department of the Interior, Bureau of Land Management, U.S. Fish and Wildlife Service, National Park Service, Environmental Protection Agency.

INDEX

C

D

E

F

G

H

I

O

P

Q

R

S

T

U

V

W

Y